Table of Contents

What's in a Word?
STRATEGIES FOR UNLOCKING MEANING

Every day you use hundreds of words. Some are simple and common—like *hello* and *the*. Others may be challenging—such as *jostle* and *preposterous*. Some are specific to a subject—such as the science term *photosynthesis*. Still others may be interesting, weird, serious, or funny, such as *bazooka, congregate, blooper,* and *icky*.

What happens when you come across an unfamiliar word in your reading? If you have a dictionary at hand, you can look up the word. If you don't have a dictionary, you still have two excellent strategies that can help you make sense of the word: **context clues** and **word parts analysis.** You will be using these strategies in every unit of this book. With practice you can master these strategies and improve your reading skills.

In the three workshops that follow, you will learn how to use these strategies to figure out the meanings of unfamiliar words:

Workshop I: Using Context Clues to Determine a Word's Meaning
In this workshop, you'll learn how to use context clues, such as definition and restatement, example, comparison, contrast, and cause and effect, as well as sentence and paragraph, or general, context clues.

Workshop II: Using Word Analysis to Determine a Word's Meaning
In this workshop, you'll learn how to break down a word into its parts. In addition, you will learn how to examine a word's origins and history in order to help you recognize unfamiliar words and to further build your vocabulary.

Workshop III: Tools to Use
In this workshop, you'll learn how to read and understand dictionary and thesaurus entries. You'll also learn how to prepare and keep a word journal that will help you to remember and keep track of the words you've learned.

Besides using these strategies for words you do not know, you can also use them for words you know but that are used in unusual ways. For example, poets and other creative writers often use words in an unusual or new way. By knowing the traditional meaning of the word, its history, and its connotations, you can figure out the writer's new use of the word.

It is important to think about the words you read. Remember to use these strategies for determining a word's meaning, and be sure to keep a word journal. Explore the meaning and history of these words until you've made them a part of your vocabulary. Make each word your own.

Workshop I
Using Context Clues to Determine a Word's Meaning

Skilled readers often use context clues to figure out a word's meaning. **Context** refers to the words or sentences surrounding the unfamiliar word. Often these clues can help you **infer,** or make a logical guess about, the word's meaning.

DEFINITION AND RESTATEMENT

Sometimes a writer will directly **define** a word, especially if the word is a technical term that may be unfamiliar to readers. Here is an example:

> The settlers reached the *piedmont*, a gently rolling foothill area between a plain and mountains.

More often, a writer will **restate** the meaning of a word in a less precise form than a dictionary definition. Notice how the writer of this sentence uses restatement.

> The king's laws were often arbitrary; in other words, he made rules based on how he felt at the moment.

The meaning of *arbitrary*—"based on one's sudden desires or notions"—becomes clear from the restatement in the second part of the sentence. Definition and restatement are often signaled by punctuation (note the comma in the first example) and by certain key words and phrases, as shown in the following chart.

Words That Signal Definition and Restatement		
which	is/are	or
this means	that is	also known as
in other words	is/are called	

EXAMPLE

The context in which a word appears may include one or more **examples** that are clues to the word's meaning. In the following sentence, note the phrase *such as,* which signals that one or more examples of the unfamiliar word *crustaceans* will follow.

> Our science class is studying *crustaceans*, such as shrimp, crabs, and lobsters.

Read the examples and note what they have in common. From this list you can conclude that *crustaceans* are a group of water animals that have a hard shell and jointed legs. The words and phrases in the following chart often signal an example.

Words That Signal Examples		
like	for example	other
including	for instance	this
such as	especially	these
		these include

COMPARISON

Sometimes the meanings of words are revealed through **comparisons** with other, familiar words or ideas in the sentence. By noting the similarities between the things described, you can get an idea of the meaning of the unfamiliar word. A comparison is often signaled by one of these key words or phrases. In the sentence below, the word *like* signals a comparison.

> The *amethyst,* like other precious stones known for hardness, cannot be cut with a knife or scratched by glass.

The comparison context clue—*like other precious stones known for hardness*—clearly indicates that an *amethyst* is a type of precious stone. Comparisons are often signaled by one of the key words and phrases shown in the following chart.

Words That Signal Comparisons		
like	also	resembling
likewise	identical	similar to
as	in the same way	similarly

CONTRAST

Sometimes the meaning of a word is revealed through **contrast.** When two words are in contrast, they have opposite meanings. By noting the similarities and differences between the things described, you can get an idea of the meaning of the unfamiliar word. In the following sentence, the phrase *in sharp contrast to* signals a contrast.

> Lincoln's Gettysburg Address was *concise,* in sharp *contrast* to the long-winded, two-hour speech that preceded it.

You can assume that a *concise* speech is the opposite of a *long-winded, two-hour speech*. A *concise* speech is a brief one. The following chart lists key words and phrases that signal a contrast.

Words That Signal Contrasts		
unlike	on the other hand	in contrast to
but	instead of	on the contrary
although	however	different from

CAUSE AND EFFECT

Another type of context clue is **cause and effect.** The cause of an action or event may be stated using an unfamiliar word. If, however, the effect is stated in familiar terms, it can help you understand the unfamiliar word. Consider the following example.

> Because the weeds in my garden are so *profuse,* I can no longer see the flowers.

In this sentence, the cause—the profuse weeds—leads to an effect—not being able to see the flowers. This indicates that *profuse* must mean "a great quantity." The following chart lists common key words and phrases that may signal cause and effect.

Words That Signal Cause and Effect		
because	consequently	therefore
so	since	as a result

INFERENCE FROM GENERAL CONTEXT

Often the clues to the meaning of an unfamiliar word are in the sentences that surround the word. Sometimes the clue may be several sentences away from the sentence containing the unfamiliar word, either in the same paragraph or in the next. In this case, you will need to continue reading until you find the clue and then infer, or make a logical guess about, the word's meaning. Study the following example:

> By the middle of the school year, Bob started to see the *fallacy* in his thinking. He had thought that because he was bright, he could get good grades in his classes without much work. Now he realized he had been mistaken. If he were going to get A's at this school, he would have to work very hard.

Continue reading until you find the clue to the meaning of *fallacy*. The clue appears in the description *he had been mistaken,* which suggests that *fallacy* means "error."

Sometimes the supporting details in a paragraph must be examined together to help you infer the meaning of an unfamiliar word. In the following paragraph, note the series of descriptive details that follows the unfamiliar word *chaos.*

> The government was in a state of *chaos*. Nobody knew who was in charge. The president had not been seen for three days, and other officials were giving orders. Many citizens disobeyed the curfews. Army tanks moved into the capital city to control the crowds, but the soldiers disobeyed their commanders and refused to attack the people.

The details that appear thoughout the paragraph help you draw the conclusion that *chaos* means "disorder and extreme confusion."

APPLICATION: Determining Meaning from Context

Each of the following sentences and paragraphs contains an italicized word you may not know. Determine the meaning of the word by using context clues. Write the definition in the blank.

1. A large portion of Brazil is *savanna*, an area of grassland and scattered trees with year-round warm temperatures.

_____

2. The twins, Timmy and Tammy, were as *frolicsome* as two kittens with a ball of yarn.

_____

3. Although Erica had been speedy and energetic in track practice, on the day of her race she felt *sluggish*.

_____

4. Hercules faced a horrible *ordeal*. He had twelve tasks, or labors, that he had to perform. The first labor was to kill a lion that no weapon could harm. The second was to kill a creature with nine heads, called the Hydra. Perhaps the most dangerous task was to travel down to the underworld and bring back a terrible three-headed dog alive.

_____

5. An examination showed that Phil was *myopic*. The doctor gave him eyeglasses to help him see things at a distance better.

_____

6. Beginning in the eighth century, ships full of *Vikings* invaded the neighboring regions of northern Europe around the Baltic and the North Sea. Known for attacking peaceful settlements without warning, these northern warriors spread terror and fear throughout Europe for two centuries. As seafaring invaders from the Scandinavian regions, they robbed churches and monasteries, raided villages, and perfected their shipbuilding techniques.

_____

7. If they had a choice, most people would probably prefer a *democratic* society, one in which all citizens can vote and have a say in their government.

_____

8. The planets in our solar system have an orbit that is an *ellipse*, a shape that looks like a flattened circle or an egg on its side.

_____

Workshop II
Using Word Analysis to Determine a Word's Meaning

Most words are made up of various combinations of the following word parts: prefix, suffix, base word, and root. Therefore, one way to determine a word's meaning is to break down the word into its parts and figure out the meaning of each part. In order to do this type of word analysis, it is useful to understand the basic terms for the different types of parts. In this workshop, you will learn about the various parts and how they create the meanings of words.

BASE WORDS

A **base word** is a complete word that can stand alone. The word *fear* is an example. Other words or word parts may be added to base words to form new words. The example below shows how adding a word part to the base word **fear** can form a new word.

fear + -ful = fearful

You can form a **compound word** by connecting two base words. The meaning of the new compound word is often, but not always, related to the meanings of the base words.

skate + board = skateboard

PREFIXES

A **prefix** is a word part attached to the beginning of a base word or a word part. It does not stand alone. In addition, prefixes alter the meaning of the base word or word part. Note the following example.

(Prefix) (Base Word) (New Word)

un- ("not") + fair ("just") = unfair ("not just")

By knowing that the prefix *un-* means "not," you can then figure out the meaning of many words to which that prefix has been added. Similarly, if you know the meaning of other common prefixes, such as *re-*, *mid-*, and *dis-*, you will have a clue to the meanings of many unfamiliar words to which those prefixes have been added. Determine the meaning of each of the following words that begin with the prefix *re-*, which means "back" or "again."

react recharge rebound

reassure recapture recall

The prefixes *un-* and *re-* are the most common in the English language. Now, look at the following list of a few other common prefixes and brainstorm words you know that begin with them.

in- dis- non- over-

mis- sub- pre- inter-

For definitions of these and other common prefixes, refer to pages 233–234.

SUFFIXES

A **suffix** is a word part attached to the end of a base word or word part. The suffix usually determines the word's part of speech—that is, whether the word is a noun, verb, adjective, or adverb. Once you know the effect that a suffix will have on a word, you can figure out the word's meaning and how it is best used in a sentence. In the following example, notice how the different suffixes change the word's part of speech and give it a new meaning.

real (base word) + -ity (noun suffix) = reality (noun)

real + -ize (verb suffix) = realize (verb)

real + -ly (adverb suffix) = really (adverb)

The spelling of a word may change when you add an inflected ending. Note the following common inflected endings and their effects on words.

Inflected Endings	Effect on Base Word	Examples
-s, -es	changes the number of a noun (from one to more than one)	ladder + -s = ladders circus + -es = circuses
-d, -ed	changes verb tense (from present to past)	skate + -d = skated walk + -ed = walked
-ing	changes verb tense (ongoing action)	jump + -ing = jumping like + -ing = liking
-er	changes the degree of comparison in modifiers (more but not most)	sick + -er = sicker easy + -er = easier
-est	changes the degree of comparison in modifiers (the most)	sick + -est = sickest easy + -est = easiest

The word **affix** is a general term that refers to both prefixes and suffixes. You can create many words simply by adding different prefixes and/or suffixes to one base word. How many words can you make from the word parts below?

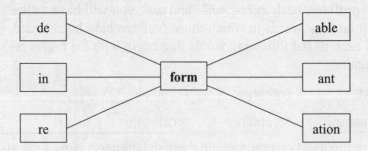

For definitions of these affixes and other common prefixes and suffixes, refer to pages 233–236.

Workshop III
Tools to Use

USING REFERENCE SOURCES

You will often need to use **basic reference sources**, such as a dictionary and a thesaurus, to help you learn new words and enhance the strategies and techniques for unlocking word meaning on your own. Below are some tips for using these sources.

DICTIONARY: A **dictionary** can tell you more than just what a word means. Look at the following dictionary entries to see some of the many details a dictionary can provide about a word.

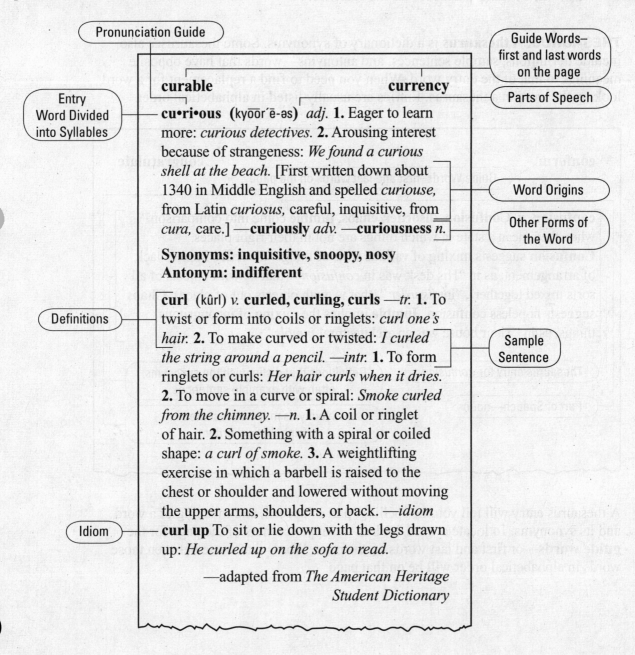

Pronunciation Guide

Guide Words—
first and last words
on the page

Entry
Word Divided
into Syllables

Parts of Speech

curable   **currency**

cu•ri•ous (kyŏŏr´ē-əs) *adj.* **1.** Eager to learn
more: *curious detectives.* **2.** Arousing interest
because of strangeness: *We found a curious
shell at the beach.* [First written down about
1340 in Middle English and spelled *curiouse,*
from Latin *curiosus,* careful, inquisitive, from
cura, care.] —**curiously** *adv.* —**curiousness** *n.*

Word Origins

Other Forms of
the Word

**Synonyms: inquisitive, snoopy, nosy
Antonym: indifferent**

Definitions

curl (kûrl) *v.* **curled, curling, curls** —*tr.* **1.** To
twist or form into coils or ringlets: *curl one's
hair.* **2.** To make curved or twisted: *I curled
the string around a pencil.* —*intr.* **1.** To form
ringlets or curls: *Her hair curls when it dries.*
2. To move in a curve or spiral: *Smoke curled
from the chimney.* —*n.* **1.** A coil or ringlet
of hair. **2.** Something with a spiral or coiled
shape: *a curl of smoke.* **3.** A weightlifting
exercise in which a barbell is raised to the
chest or shoulder and lowered without moving
the upper arms, shoulders, or back. —*idiom*

Sample
Sentence

Idiom

curl up To sit or lie down with the legs drawn
up: *He curled up on the sofa to read.*

—adapted from *The American Heritage
Student Dictionary*

To find a word in a dictionary, use the **guide words,** the two words that appear at the top of each dictionary page. The first word in the pair is the first word on the page, and the second word is the last word on the page.

Once you locate the word, you may find that there is more than one meaning. If a word has more than one meaning, how do you choose the right one from the dictionary? Use the following tips to determine the definition that is appropriate to the context in which you find the word.

- Rule out definitions that don't make sense, given what you're reading.
- Try adding words to the sentence that go with each particular meaning of the word.
- Pick the definition that best fits the sentence.

THESAURUS: A **thesaurus** is a dictionary of synonyms. Some thesauruses also include definitions, sample sentences, and antonyms—words that have opposite meanings to that of the entry word. When you need to find a replacement for a word, look up the word in a thesaurus. Entries are usually listed in alphabetical order.

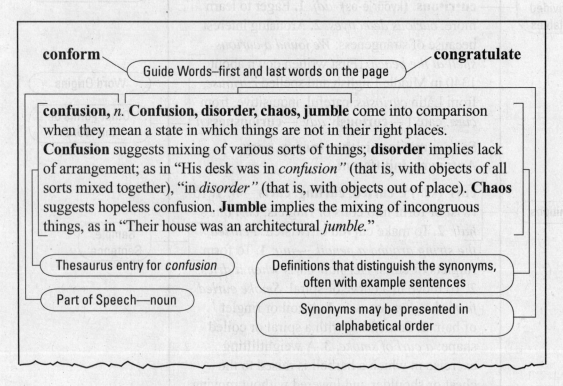

A thesaurus entry will tell you the spelling, part of speech, and meaning of a word and its synonyms. To locate a word, look in the upper corners of the page for the **guide words**—or first and last words on the page. Words that come between those words in alphabetical order will be on that page.

KEEP A WORD JOURNAL

Whenever you are reading, jot down any word that is unfamiliar or that seems vague in meaning to you. Use a small notebook in which to write the words. If you don't have a dictionary nearby, find one later and look up the word. Write down the meaning next to the word in your journal and then go back to the text where you found the word. Does the meaning seem clearer to you now?

When Abby won the spelling contest, the thunderous applause was *gratifying* to her. Even days later, she was thrilled by her achievement.

> Use context clues to guess at the word's meaning. Then look up the word in the dictionary.

From the context of this sentence, the word *gratifying* appears to mean enjoyable or satisfying. To find it in the dictionary, you will need to look up the word *gratify,* which is a verb that means "to please or satisfy." In this case, the added suffix *-ing* turns the word into an adjective. Think of another sentence in which you can use the word.

REMEMBERING NEW WORDS

The following strategies will help you remember new words.

- In a journal or small notebook, list each new word as you find it. Note where you found the word. Later, look up the word in a dictionary and add its definition.

- Think of related words.

- Use the word right away at least three times in your writing or conversations.

- Create a device to help you remember its meaning. This could be a tongue twister, a rhyme, or a catchy phrase or sentence.

As you go through the exercises in this book, add words to a word bank, which you can keep in your journal of words. Your bank entries might look like this:

Word Journal

Word	Meaning	Example in a Sentence
legend, n.	a short description or key to the various markings on a map	The map's legend indicated that the roads marked in red were the scenic routes.

APPLICATION: Using a Thesaurus and a Dictionary

Read the following entries from a thesaurus. Then choose a more exact synonym to replace the underlined word in each sentence. Write the word in the blank. Check your responses by looking the word up in a dictionary.

question, *v.* **Question, ask, interrogate, examine, query, inquire, quiz** come into comparison when they mean the act of seeking information. **Question, ask, query,** and **inquire** are broad, general terms. **Quiz** implies authority or threat; **interrogate** implies extreme threat or assumption of guilt. **Examine** implies a critical look.

neglect, *v.* **Neglect, omit, ignore, forget** come into comparison when they mean to pass over without proper attention. **Neglect** implies intentional or unintentional failure to pay attention, as in, "Don't *neglect* to pay your rent." **Ignore** implies intentional disregard. **Omit** implies leaving out part of a whole, as in, "*Omit* the last chapter and concentrate on the first three." **Forget** stresses loss of memory.

common, *adj.* **Common, ordinary, popular, familiar** come into comparison when they mean being of a generally known character. **Common** implies the lack of distinguishing qualities, as in, "That's a very *common* error." **Ordinary** implies being in the regular order of things. **Familiar** stresses being generally known or easily recognized; **popular** expresses widespread favor.

examine   **1.** At our next meeting, we will <u>question</u> our club rules.

forget   **2.** It may rain, so don't <u>neglect</u> to bring your raincoat.

familiar   **3.** His face is so <u>common</u> that I know I've seen him before.

omite   **4.** If you <u>neglect</u> your last name on your paper, your test will be discarded.

interrogate   **5.** My mother is sure to <u>question</u> me for hours about the broken vase.

popular   **6.** That <u>common</u> song is on every radio station this month.

ignore   **7.** To <u>neglect</u> traffic signals is to ask for trouble.

forget   **8.** How could you <u>neglect</u> that our report is due today?

ordinary   **9.** It was just a <u>common</u> day, with nothing unusual happening.

ask   **10.** Where may I <u>question</u> about a lost umbrella?

Feature: Synonyms and Antonyms

WHAT IS IT?

Synonyms are words that are similar in meaning. For example, all of the words following the sentence below are synonyms for *ran*.

I **ran** up the beach.   *jogged*   *hurried*   *dashed*   *raced*

Antonyms are words that are opposite in meaning. The two boldfaced words in this sentence are antonyms.

David **shunned** any outdoor activity, but Sarah **welcomed** it.

A **thesaurus**—a reference book that lists synonyms—can help you choose the word that best expresses what you want to say. It often lists antonyms as well.

WHY IT MATTERS

Synonyms and antonyms can help you distinguish shades of meaning. When you know the synonyms and antonyms for words, you can better understand the texts you read. You can also be more precise in the words you choose in your own writing.

EXERCISE 1: Identify Synonyms

For each boldfaced word, find the synonym in the word list that could be used in the sentence. Write the synonym in the space provided. Use a thesaurus or dictionary if needed.

complete	cure	empty	free	huge
nervousness	package	protection	worry	wrong

1. This **parcel** is too heavy to go first class. _____

2. Don't **brood** about your mistakes; just try to learn from them. _____

3. I think the best **remedy** for a cold is sleep. _____

4. The best **defense** is the truth. _____

5. That old **vacant** lot is now a playground. _____

6. My mother spends her **leisure** time reading mystery novels. _____

7. Vera did **thorough** research for her report. _____

8. Jeff felt great **anxiety** before his speech. _____

9. The flute player hit a **sour** note during the performance. _____

10. Ellie's room is a **monstrous** mess. _____

EXERCISE 2: Identify Antonyms

For each item, choose the correct antonym for the boldfaced word. Use a thesaurus or a dictionary if needed.

sloppily	mature	primary	strict	neat
fresh	unfinished	rainy	destroy	despises

1. What you wear is a **secondary** matter; how you act is of _____ importance.

2. I **admire** Trey, but Allison _____ him.

3. The den is nice and _____; however, your bedroom is incredibly **messy.**

4. Sam's father is _____, but Sara's is very **lenient.**

5. This bread is **stale.** Where can I get some that is _____?

6. I **create** sand castles, but my little brother can only _____ them.

7. Is your homework **complete,** or is it still _____?

8. How **childish!** I wish he would be more _____.

9. Stella's work was done **neatly,** but mine was done _____.

10. Will the weather be **sunny** or _____ today?

EXERCISE 3: Make Words Your Own

Synonyms and antonyms can give you a fuller understanding of a word's meaning. For each of the words in the left column, write at least one synonym and one antonym in the appropriate columns.

Target Words	Synonym	Antonym
warmth		
familiar		
clumsy		
create		
daring		
lift		
adult		
courtesy		

LESSON 1

Common Prefixes and Base Words I

Target Words	Prefix	Meaning of Prefix
disapprove, v.	dis-	not; opposite of
disloyal, adj.		
disobey, v.		
impatient, adj.	im-/in-	not; opposite of
impolite, adj.		
independent, adj.		
inexact, adj.		
misfortune, n.	mis-	bad, badly; wrong, wrongly
misjudge, v.		
unequal, adj.	un-	not; opposite of
unfamiliar, adj.		
unstable, adj.		

GETTING STARTED

Breaking a word into its parts can help you figure out its meaning. Two important word parts are **prefixes** and **base words.**

- A **prefix** is a word part attached to the beginning of a word or a word part.

- A **base word** is a complete word that can stand alone.

In this lesson you will learn about the prefixes *dis-, im-, in-, mis-,* and *un-*. These prefixes are commonly called the "not" and "bad" prefixes because they often help express negative actions, attitudes, and conditions. The example shows how adding one of these prefixes to a base word can create a new word with a different meaning.

(prefix that means "not")   (base word that means "right" or "proper")

in + correct = incorrect

(word that means "not correct; wrong; not proper")

I. Practice the Words

EXERCISE 1: Understand Prefixes

Here are three target words. Circle the prefix in each word. Think of two other words that share the same prefix and write them in the spaces shown. Do not use any target words.

1. disloyal   word 1: _____   word 2: _____

2. inexact   word 1: _____   word 2: _____

3. unequal   word 1: _____   word 2: _____

EXERCISE 2: Break It Down

For each target word in the first column, draw a line between the prefix and the base word. Then match each target word with its correct meaning in the second column. Write the letter of the correct meaning in the space provided. Use a dictionary if necessary. The first one has been done for you as an example.

1. disapprove   _c_   a. bad luck

2. disloyal   _____   b. to make a wrong decision

3. disobey   _____   c. to dislike or reject

4. impatient   _____   d. not known or recognizable

5. impolite   _____   e. not trustworthy

6. independent   _____   f. not calm

7. inexact   _____   g. not having the same value

8. misfortune   _____   h. not accurate

9. misjudge   _____   i. not well-mannered

10. unequal   _____   j. to break orders or rules

11. unfamiliar   _____   k. not firmly placed

12. unstable   _____   l. not controlled by others

EXERCISE 3: Match Words to Context

Select a target word from the list to complete each sentence and write the word on the line. Use your knowledge of context clues such as contrast, restatement, or cause and effect to help you determine the correct word. Use each word only once. Some words will not be used.

| disapprove(s) | disobey(s) | independent | inexact | impatient |
| misfortune | misjudge(s) | unequal | unfamiliar | unstable |

1. Mrs. Nash gave each child the same amount of popcorn, not an _____ share.

2. Mark often _____ his parents' wishes, unlike his sister Ann who is respectful.

3. The neighborhood Hector visited was _____, that is, unknown to him.

4. Because the wait at the doctor's office was so long, Mr. Ford became _____.

5. The gourmet chef was very careful in her measurements, not _____.

6. As a result of her poor eyesight, Selma often _____ how far away things are.

EXERCISE 4: Analyze Context and Meaning

On the line before each statement, write *T* if the statement is true. Write *F* if it is false. Use your knowledge of the boldfaced target words to help you decide.

_____ **1.** Mathematicians often work with **inexact** numbers.

_____ **2.** A friend who reveals a secret may be considered **disloyal.**

_____ **3.** Most parents **disapprove** of children eating healthy snacks.

_____ **4.** To lose one's job would be a **misfortune.**

_____ **5.** Buildings made with steel are usually **unstable.**

_____ **6. Independent** people care for themselves.

_____ **7.** A square has four **unequal** sides.

_____ **8.** People who talk during a movie are **impolite.**

_____ **9.** Drivers are often **impatient** during traffic jams.

_____ **10.** Students sometimes **misjudge** the time to leave for school and are late for class.

_____ **11.** Most people feel relaxed in **unfamiliar** surroundings.

_____ **12.** Cooperative patients **disobey** the advice of doctors.

EXERCISE 5: Understand Synonyms

Write the letter of the word that is closest in meaning to the boldfaced target word.

_____ **1. disapprove** **a.** allow **b.** overlook **c.** reject **d.** tolerate

_____ **2. disloyal** **a.** false **b.** greedy **c.** faithful **d.** generous

_____ **3. disobey** **a.** rebel **b.** conform **c.** react **d.** follow

_____ **4. impatient** **a.** tolerant **b.** relaxed **c.** cheerful **d.** anxious

_____ **5. impolite** **a.** considerate **b.** rude **c.** skillful **d.** clumsy

_____ **6. inexact** **a.** accurate **b.** focused **c.** rough **d.** precise

_____ **7. misfortune** **a.** kindness **b.** relief **c.** cruelty **d.** hardship

_____ **8. unequal** **a.** lopsided **b.** balanced **c.** same **d.** hilly

_____ **9. unfamiliar** **a.** dull **b.** strange **c.** known **d.** lively

_____ **10. unstable** **a.** partial **b.** complete **c.** wobbly **d.** steady

EXERCISE 6: Use Target Words in Writing

On a separate sheet of paper, write a brief review of a television show, movie, or musical group that you dislike. Make sure to identify and explain the qualities that you don't like. Use at least three target words in your review.

II. Vocabulary Challenge

EXERCISE 7: Extend Your Vocabulary

Match each prefix with its appropriate base word. Use each new word in a sentence. Consult a dictionary if necessary.

    honest   complete   possible   favor   understand   welcome

1. *dis-* _____

sentence: _____

2. *im-* _____

sentence: _____

3. *in-* _____

sentence: _____

4. *mis-* _____

sentence: _____

5. *un-* _____

sentence: _____

6. *dis-* _____

sentence: _____

Wordsmart: Spelling

The spelling of the prefix *in-* changes depending on the word that follows it. When the prefix *in-* comes before a word beginning with the letters *m* or *p*, it is spelled *im-*, as in *impatient*.

LESSON 2 Words That Describe People

Target Words

coy, *adj.* shy in a playful way

fret, *v.* to be vexed or troubled; worry

gesture, *n., v.* a body movement that expresses an idea; to make gestures

insistent, *adj.* continuing firmly and stubbornly

mournful, *adj.* sorrowful; expressing grief

nag, *v.* to bother by constant scolding or finding fault

perplexed, *adj.* filled with confusion

resourceful, *adj.* able to act effectively in almost any situation

sheepish, *adj.* embarrassed as if knowingly at fault

taunt, *v.* to make fun of; to mock

tidy, *adj.* orderly and neat in appearance

unruly, *adj.* difficult to control

GETTING STARTED

Finding the right word to explain someone's behavior can be difficult. The target words in this lesson can help you expand your vocabulary for describing the behavior of people you know or characters that you read about.

I. Practice the Words

EXERCISE 1: Solve a Paragraph Puzzle

Using the target words and paragraph clues, fill in the blank spaces below. Use each word only once. Be sure the words fit grammatically into the sentences.

Malcolm was standing in a long line at the grocery store with his mother. Behind him

was a woman who looked tired and _____ . Her _____

children were throwing candy bars on the floor. She made a _____ at

them to stop, but they stared at her with a _____ look on their faces, as

if they did not understand what she meant. Malcolm wondered if she was the kind of

mother who would _____ at her children, always telling them what to do

and when. He thought she might be _____ that they always be neat and

_____ , as she looked like the type who would _____ over

cleanliness. Just then, one of the girls looked at Malcolm with a _____

smile. He stuck out his tongue to _____ her, but then he felt

_____ about acting as badly as they did. The _____ child

grabbed the first thing she could find—a pack of gum—and threw it at him.

EXERCISE 2: Match Words to Context

Circle the letter of the word that best completes the sentence.

1. Even though she blushed and acted _____, you could see that she liked him.
   a. resourceful   **b.** mournful   **c.** tidy   **d.** coy

2. A neat desk is probably an indication of a _____ person.
   a. coy   **b.** sheepish   **c.** tidy   **d.** perplexed

3. His parents would _____ him about doing his homework every night after dinner.
   a. gesture   **b.** nag   **c.** fret   **d.** taunt

4. When she refused to obey her mother, the _____ child was sent to bed.
   a. coy   **b.** resourceful   **c.** unruly   **d.** insistent

5. She was likely to succeed in any situation because she was _____.
   a. resourceful   **b.** mournful   **c.** sheepish   **d.** unruly

6. With a _____ grin, the girl confessed to playing the practical joke on her friend.
   a. mournful   **b.** sheepish   **c.** coy   **d.** insistent

7. The boy liked to _____ his sister because she always reacted to his teasing.
   a. fret   **b.** insistent   **c.** taunt   **d.** gesture

8. The students felt _____ after reading the confusing instructions.
   a. mournful   **b.** sheepish   **c.** perplexed   **d.** tidy

9. The _____ dog begged everyone at the table for a scrap of meat.
   a. insistent   **b.** perplexed   **c.** coy   **d.** tidy

10. Try not to _____ over things you can't change.
   a. gesture   **b.** taunt   **c.** fret   **d.** nag

11. The teacher signaled them with a _____ that meant "sit down."
   a. gesture   **b.** resourceful   **c.** taunt   **d.** fret

12. My neighbor looked _____ for weeks after his dog died.
   a. sheepish   **b.** coy   **c.** mournful   **d.** unruly

EXERCISE 3: Use Target Words in Writing

On a separate sheet of paper, write a sentence for each of the target words listed at
the beginning of this lesson. Be sure your sentences show that you understand what
the words mean.

   EXAMPLE   tidy   *There was nothing out of place in the tidy room.*

UNIT 1

EXERCISE 4: Use Synonyms

Circle the letter of the word that is closest in meaning to the boldfaced word.

1. **nag**   a. approve   b. complain   c. shout   d. compliment
2. **mournful**   a. happy   b. loud   c. sad   d. soft
3. **fret**   a. love   b. sting   c. point   d. fuss
4. **perplexed** a. merry   b. angry   c. puzzled   d. unconcerned
5. **taunt**   a. tease   b. please   c. twist   d. confuse
6. **insistent** a. happy   b. soft   c. final   d. demanding
7. **gesture**   a. noise   b. motion   c. guest   d. cane
8. **coy**   a. skilled   b. playful   c. adaptable d. young
9. **sheepish**   a. angry   b. shy   c. rude   d. embarrassed
10. **tidy**   a. sloppy   b. nervous   c. organized d. insulting

EXERCISE 5: Identify Antonyms

Use a dictionary and a thesaurus to find an accurate antonym for each word. Record the antonym and its meaning. Be sure that the words in each pair of antonyms are the same part of speech.

Target Word	Antonym	Meaning of Antonym
coy, *adj.*		
fret, *v.*		
gesture, *n.*		
insistent, *adj.*		
mournful, *adj.*		
nag, *v.*		
perplexed, *adj.*		
resourceful, *adj.*		
sheepish, *adj.*		
taunt, *v.*		
tidy, *adj.*		
unruly, *adj.*		

EXERCISE 6: Speaking

Discuss one of the following topics with a small group of your classmates.

1. Think of a character in a story that you have read whom you could describe with one or more of the target words. Explain to your classmates why you would describe the character this way.

2. Think of a friend whom you could describe using one or more of the target words. Explain to your classmates why you would describe your friend this way.

II. Vocabulary Challenge

EXERCISE 7: Extend Your Vocabulary

Create new words from the target words by finding words within the target words, or by adding word parts to make new words. Although these new words may not have anything in common with the target word, check their meanings in the dictionary to see if they do.

EXAMPLE   unruly   *rule, ruler, ruling*

1. coy _____

2. fret _____

3. insistent _____

4. mournful _____

5. nag _____

6. perplexed _____

7. resourceful _____

8. sheepish _____

9. taunt _____

10. tidy _____

Wordsmart: Etymology
The word *fret* means "to worry." It comes from the Middle English word *freten,* which means "to devour." The current meaning probably came from the idea that worry "eats up" your thoughts. Look up the word *fret* in the dictionary. What other meanings does the word have? Do they all have the same origin?

LESSON 4 Words That Describe Actions

Target Words

assume, *v.* to accept as true

banish, *v.* to send away

comprehend, *v.* to understand

conclude, *v.* to finish; to make up one's mind

depart, *v.* to go away

jostle, *v.* to elbow one's way through a crowd; to push or bump into

lounge, *v.* to behave in a lazy manner

misinform, *v.* to tell the wrong facts or details

outrage, *n., v.* a shocking or offensive act; to offend or shock

ponder, *v.* to think carefully about

slouch, *n., v.* a drooping position with bad posture; to droop or show bad posture

waver, *v.* to move unsteadily; to hesitate

GETTING STARTED

People's actions do not include only physical activities; they can include mental activities such as making a decision or telling a lie. The target words in this lesson can expand your vocabulary for describing both mental and physical actions that people take in real life and in literature. The words can also help you describe your own actions or those of characters in stories and plays.

I. Practice the Words

EXERCISE 1: Solve a Paragraph Puzzle

Using the target words, fill in all the blank spaces in this paragraph. Use each word only once. Be sure the words fit grammatically into the sentences.

Clark likes to take it easy. On weekends he will _____ till noon in his pajamas.

His favorite position is a _____. Before going anywhere, he will

_____ his decision for a long time, and even then he will _____.

He especially hates going to parties where he has to _____ through crowds.

To get him to her party, Jill had to _____ him by saying she had invited only

ten people. When he arrived and saw over fifty, he felt _____. He could not

_____ why so many people would all want to be in one place. He did not wait

for the party to _____ but instead decided to _____ early. The

next day, Jill phoned to ask why he had left so early. "I _____ that you enjoy big

parties," Clark told her, "but I do not. The next time you trick me into coming to a party, I will

_____ you from my circle of friends."

EXERCISE 2: Match Words to Context

Circle the letter of the word that best completes each sentence. Use your knowledge of sentence clues to help you choose your answer.

1. When you see lightning, you can _____ that thunder will probably follow.
   a. conclude   **b.** depart   **c.** ponder   **d.** misinform

2. The queen decided to _____ the traitor to another land rather than order his death.
   a. outrage   **b.** waver   **c.** depart   **d.** banish

3. Students sometimes _____ in their chairs to try to avoid being called on.
   a. lounge   **b.** slouch   **c.** waver   **d.** ponder

4. If others _____ us about the facts, we are likely to reach false conclusions.
   a. assume   **b.** comprehend   **c.** jostle   **d.** misinform

5. A stubborn woman, she takes a position and does not _____.
   a. assume   **b.** jostle   **c.** waver   **d.** lounge

6. For some students, complicated new ideas are hard to _____.
   a. comprehend   **b.** assume   **c.** conclude   **d.** jostle

7. Things that go against our beliefs sometimes _____ us.
   a. misinform   **b.** comprehend   **c.** outrage   **d.** assume

8. Did you go for a jog, or did you just _____ around the park with your friends?
   a. depart   **b.** banish   **c.** conclude   **d.** lounge

9. Try not to _____ anyone as you take your luggage through the crowded station.
   a. banish   **b.** jostle   **c.** outrage   **d.** ponder

10. I _____ he is telling me the truth, but I do not know for sure.
    a. comprehend   **b.** assume   **c.** misinform   **d.** waver

11. I will _____ from the south gate.
    a. depart   **b.** slouch   **c.** waver   **d.** lounge

12. Her lecture gave us much to _____.
    a. misinform   **b.** assume   **c.** outrage   **d.** ponder

EXERCISE 3: Use Target Words in Writing

On a separate sheet of paper, write a sentence for each of the target words listed at the beginning of this lesson. Be sure your sentences show that you understand what the words mean.

EXAMPLE   ponder   *You can ponder the poem for hours and still not know what it means.*

EXERCISE 4: Use Synonyms

For each sentence, suggest a target word to replace the boldfaced word without changing the meaning of the sentence. Write the target word on the line after the sentence.

assume	banish	comprehend	conclude	depart	jostle
lounge	misinform	outrage	ponder	slouch	waver

1. It is sometimes hard to **understand** what Mara is saying. _____

2. At what hour will the dance contest **end**? _____

3. The mold and germs in this cafeteria are a terrible **offense**! _____

4. Will Carly stick with her plan, or will she **falter**? _____

5. The train is scheduled to **leave** at 10:30 in the morning. _____

6. Fashion models keep their backs erect and never **stoop.** _____

7. The artist likes to **consider** his plans before starting to paint. _____

8. The village elders decided to **cast out** the thief. _____

9. I tried not to **shove** people as I made my way to my seat. _____

10. He did not intend to **deceive** her about the facts. _____

11. We can **relax** on the beach all afternoon. _____

12. Since the explorer has been missing for six years, shall we **presume** he is dead? _____

EXERCISE 5: Identify Antonyms

Circle the letter of the word that is most nearly the opposite of the boldfaced word.

1. **comprehend**   a. answer   b. limit   c. misjudge   d. misunderstand

2. **conclude**   a. begin   b. permit   c. respond   d. understand

3. **depart**   a. hint   b. interlock   c. divide   d. arrive

4. **outrage**   a. offend   b. puzzle   c. please   d. disconnect

5. **waver**   a. quiver   b. persist   c. hesitate   d. whisper

6. **slouch**   a. sleep   b. stand   c. creep   d. weaken

7. **lounge**   a. work   b. wither   c. remain   d. ease

8. **banish**   a. publish   b. enrage   c. invite   d. insult

9. **assume**   a. question   b. combine   c. allow   d. comfort

10. **misinform**   a. deceive   b. delete   c. clarify   d. revise

EXERCISE 6: Speaking

Discuss one of the following topics with a small group of your classmates. Use at least three target words in your discussion.

1. Describe the actions of a character in a story. Explain what the character's actions show about his or her personality.

2. Describe your own behavior. Focus on either mental or physical actions.

II. Vocabulary Challenge

EXERCISE 7: Word Play

Use the clues to figure out which target word to put on each series of lines. Put one letter on each line. When you are done, the shaded box down the center will spell out a target word that means "to get it."

EXAMPLE   figure to be true   <u>a</u> <u>s</u> <u>s</u> <u>u</u> <u>m</u> <u>e</u>

Clues

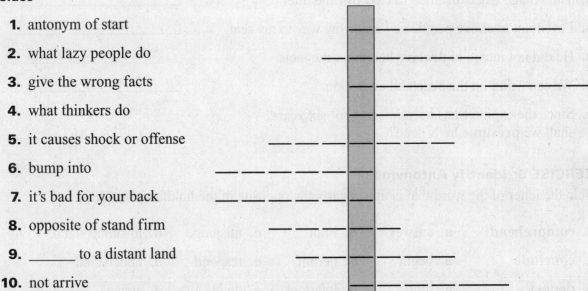

1. antonym of start

2. what lazy people do

3. give the wrong facts

4. what thinkers do

5. it causes shock or offense

6. bump into

7. it's bad for your back

8. opposite of stand firm

9. _____ to a distant land

10. not arrive

Wordsmart: Etymology

The word *banish* entered English from the Old French language during the Middle Ages. It is historically related to the word *ban,* which means "to order not to do or appear." Look up the word *ban* in a dictionary. What other meanings did *ban* once have? What do those meanings suggest about the meaning of *banish*?

Check Your Knowledge: Unit 1

By now you have added 48 new words to your vocabulary. Test your ability to use these words in the following exercises.

A. Determine Meaning from Context

On the line before each sentence, write the letter of the word or phrase that is closest in meaning to the boldfaced target word. Use the context clues to help you decide.

_____ **1.** I **assume** Lou's facts are accurate, although I do not know for sure.
    a. ask   **b.** contradict   **c.** accept as true   **d.** fail to believe

_____ **2.** If your clocks **misinform** you about the time, you may miss the bus.
    a. chime   **b.** grow old   **c.** research facts   **d.** give wrong facts

_____ **3.** The funeral was a **mournful** occasion, with many guests in tears.
    a. happy   **b.** sad   **c.** formal   **d.** informal

_____ **4.** The nanny had trouble getting the **unruly** children to behave.
    a. wild   **b.** obedient   **c.** tangled   **d.** easy to control

_____ **5.** My brother likes to **lounge** around the house instead of doing chores.
    a. nod   **b.** study   **c.** be active   **d.** be lazy

_____ **6.** Experience has taught me to **ponder** for a long time before making decisions.
    a. decide   **b.** experience   **c.** think carefully   **d.** hit with a hammer

_____ **7.** Sheila flirts boldly, but her sister wins more interest by being **coy.**
    a. angry   **b.** boastful   **c.** wisely silent   **d.** playfully shy

_____ **8.** Our art teacher values neatness and insists that we keep our supplies **tidy.**
    a. orderly   **b.** fresh   **c.** bowl shaped   **d.** poorly organized

_____ **9.** Speaking while chewing is considered **impolite** behavior.
    a. kind   **b.** shrewd   **c.** unintelligent   **d.** rude

_____ **10.** A new hairdo will **transform** her from a pretty woman to a beautiful one.
    a. trim   **b.** change   **c.** stand behind   **d.** become attractive

B. Match Ideas

Using your knowledge of the target words, choose the best answer to each question.
Write the letter of your choice on the line before the question.

_____ 1. Which of these people would a king or queen most likely **banish**?

       a. a **disloyal** person   **b.** a **resourceful** person   **c.** a **tidy** person

_____ 2. Which expression shows that someone does not **comprehend** something?

       a. a **mournful** expression   **b.** a **perplexed** expression   **c.** a **coy** expression

_____ 3. What would an **impatient** person be most likely to do?

       a. ponder something   **b. lounge** in bed   **c. jostle** someone

_____ 4. A carpenter might be **perplexed** by what kind of measurements?

       a. unruly measurements   **b. inexact** measurements   **c. insistent** measurements

_____ 5. Which feelings would tend to cause a person to **slouch**?

       a. coy feelings   **b. superhuman** feelings   **c. sheepish** feelings

C. Identify Synonyms and Antonyms

In these items, boldfaced target words are paired with other words. On the line before
each pair of words, write *S* if the words are synonyms. Write *A* if they are antonyms.

_____ 1. **conclude**/start   _____ 8. **unfamiliar**/common

_____ 2. **nag**/praise   _____ 9. **unequal**/same

_____ 3. **resourceful**/clever   _____ 10. **independent**/free

_____ 4. **taunt**/tease   _____ 11. **prearrange**/plan

_____ 5. **mournful**/ sad   _____ 12. **waver**/hesitate

_____ 6. **impolite**/ respectful   _____ 13. **unstable**/sturdy

_____ 7. **disobey**/ follow   _____ 14. **misfortune**/trouble

D. Add Base Words

Match one of the ten base words below with each italic prefix. Use each base word only once. Write the new word you have formed and define its meaning without using the base word in your definition.

exact   polite   merge   dawn   view
war   vision   approve   plant   stable

1. *in-* _____

meaning: _____

2. *trans-* _____

meaning: _____

3. *sub-* _____

meaning: _____

4. *im-* _____

meaning: _____

5. *un-* _____

meaning: _____

6. *post-* _____

meaning: _____

E. Analyze Context and Meaning

Each of the following statements contains at least one boldfaced target word. On the line before the statement, write *T* if it is true. Write *F* if it is false.

_____ **1.** An **independent** person does things on his or her own.

_____ **2.** If you **misjudge** something, you get the facts right.

_____ **3.** You can use your hands to make a **gesture.**

_____ **4.** A **postscript** is often found at the beginning of a letter.

_____ **5.** A **submarine** can **submerge** itself in the sea.

_____ **6.** Most people smile when they feel **outrage.**

_____ **7.** When people **depart** for a vacation, they travel away from home.

_____ **8.** A street **intersection** sometimes has a traffic light or a stop sign.

_____ **9.** A **predawn** walk takes place in the afternoon.

_____ **10.** A **disloyal** friend is someone you can trust.

F. Use Words in Context

On the line before each sentence, write the target word that best completes the sentence. Use each target word only once. Not all choices will be used.

superhuman	fret	insistent	taunt	unruly
conclude	misfortune	disapprove	supervision	interview

_____ **1.** The gods and goddesses had _____ powers that no one on earth had.

_____ **2.** In the _____, John answered a reporter's questions.

_____ **3.** That cruel boy likes to _____ children who are smaller than he is.

_____ **4.** Since she ate her food so quickly, we can _____ that Kay was hungry.

_____ **5.** I tried to stay home, but Suzie was so _____ that I finally agreed to come.

LESSON 6 Words from Earth Science

Target Words
avalanche, *n.* loose snow, earth, or rocks that slide down a mountain
carbon, *n.* a nonmetallic chemical element found in living and nonliving things
cavern, *n.* a large cave
deposit, *n.* sand, clay, minerals, or other material moved and placed down by the action of wind, water, volcanoes, or ice
gorge, *n.* a deep, narrow valley or pass between steep heights
molten, *adj.* turned to liquid by heat
oasis, *n.* a place in the desert where water is present and plants grow
outcrop, *n.* a mineral or rock that sticks out through the soil
ridge, *n.* a long, narrow elevation; the highest point of a hill, mountain, or mountain range
stratified, *adj.* formed in layers
sulfur, *n.* a pale yellow chemical element found widely in nature
volcanic, *n.* relating to a volcano, a vent in the earth's crust from which molten rock, gases, and other material sometimes spill out from the earth's interior

GETTING STARTED

Earth science is the study of the earth's physical environment, including its climate, bodies of water, and land forms. The target words in this lesson will expand your academic vocabulary, help you read science texts, and add to your knowledge of earth science.

I. Practice the Words

EXERCISE 1: Solve a Paragraph Puzzle

Using the target words, fill in all the blank spaces in this paragraph. Use each word only once. Be sure the words fit grammatically into the sentences.

The mountain climbers crossed the high _____ before walking down a

deep _____ that led to a dark _____. They stood outside

the opening, examining an _____ of a rock that looked like quartz. They

were surprised to see some trees, as unexpected as a green _____ in a

desert. Near the trees was _____ rock, its layers indicating the one-time

presence of water. Was the black layer in the mountain wall a _____

of _____ that was left behind by ice or water? It was certainly not

_____, for it was not pale yellow. As the climbers continued, they saw

a volcano. Black glassy material nearby had hardened from once _____

rock heated by the _____ activity. The climbers had to be careful, for loose

material could come down the mountain in a deadly _____.

UNIT 2

EXERCISE 2: Match Words to Context

Circle the letter of the word that best completes each sentence. Use your knowledge of sentence clues to help you choose your answer.

1. A large _____ could cause a deadly traffic accident on a mountain road.
   a. oasis   **b.** cavern   **c.** gorge   **d.** avalanche

2. The travelers drank from the well in the desert _____.
   a. outcrop   **b.** cavern   **c.** oasis   **d.** deposit

3. The pale yellow element _____ lets off a blue flame when it burns.
   a. avalanche   **b.** sulfur   **c.** deposit   **d.** carbon

4. Mount Saint Helens has had _____ activity in recent years.
   a. molten   **b.** volcanic   **c.** stratified   **d.** outcrop

5. Rocks with layers are said to be _____.
   a. molten   **b.** volcanic   **c.** stratified   **d.** carbon

6. The rocky _____ emerged from the earth's surface a long time ago.
   a. outcrop   **b.** cavern   **c.** avalanche   **d.** oasis

7. The inside of a hillside _____ is usually cool and damp.
   a. oasis   **b.** outcrop   **c.** sulfur   **d.** cavern

8. A river can leave behind a large _____ of sand that grows bigger every year.
   a. avalanche   **b.** deposit   **c.** oasis   **d.** cavern

9. Often dark in appearance, _____ is the basic element in coal and charcoal.
   a. carbon   **b.** sulfur   **c.** volcanic   **d.** ridge

10. The _____ between the two mountains is very deep.
    a. sulfur   **b.** gorge   **c.** outcrop   **d.** molten

11. Scientists discovered an ocean _____ 2500 meters below the surface.
    a. carbon   **b.** avalanche   **c.** ridge   **d.** oasis

12. The _____ rock had formed a cone as it cooled.
    a. sulfur   **b.** avalanche   **c.** deposit   **d.** molten

EXERCISE 3: Use Target Words in Writing

On a separate sheet of paper write a sentence for each target word listed at the beginning of this lesson. Be sure the sentences show your knowledge of earth science.

    EXAMPLE   carbon   *The chemical element carbon is represented by the letter C.*

EXERCISE 4: Use Synonyms

On each line, write the target word with a similar meaning to the boldfaced word.

_____ **1.** Can a rocky **formation** appear suddenly in the earth's surface?

_____ **2.** Many rock walls in the Grand Canyon are **layered.**

_____ **3.** Even in June there is often snow on the **crest** of the mountain.

_____ **4.** Great heat creates the **liquid** rock that pours from a volcano.

_____ **5.** Water helped to form the deep **valley** between the two mountains.

_____ **6.** The train through the Rockies may be canceled when there is a big **rockfall.**

_____ **7.** The hikers entered a large **opening** in the hillside.

_____ **8.** The **debris** left behind by the river grew larger every year.

EXERCISE 5: Determine True/False

On the line before each statement, write *T* if the statement is true. Write *F* if it is false. Use your knowledge of the boldfaced target words to help you decide.

_____ **1.** Substances containing a great deal of **carbon** are usually pale yellow.

_____ **2.** **Sulfur** is a chemical element produced in laboratories but not found in nature.

_____ **3.** An **outcrop** appears above the soil, not below it.

_____ **4.** A **stratified** rock may have layers of different colors.

_____ **5.** A **gorge** is always very wide.

_____ **6.** Wind may leave a **deposit** of sand behind.

_____ **7.** An **avalanche** could bring danger to a mountain village.

_____ **8.** The lowest point on a hill or a mountain is called a **ridge.**

_____ **9.** During **volcanic** activity, **molten** rock sometimes erupts from inside the earth.

_____ **10.** You are likely to find an **oasis** at the bottom of a cavern.

EXERCISE 6: Speaking

Discuss one of the following topics with a small group of your classmates. Use at least two target words in your discussion.

1. Discuss some of the common chemical elements and their properties.

2. Discuss some characteristics of mountains or volcanoes with your classmates.

UNIT 2

EXERCISE 7: Find the Unrelated Word

Write the letter of the word that is not related in meaning to the other words in the set.

_____ 1. **a.** molten   **b.** solid   **c.** melted   **d.** liquid

_____ 2. **a.** hilltop   **b.** hole   **c.** cave   **d.** cavern

_____ 3. **a.** gorge   **b.** valley   **c.** canyon   **d.** desert

_____ 4. **a.** ridge   **b.** shore   **c.** top   **d.** peak

II. Vocabulary Challenge

EXERCISE 8: Extend Your Vocabulary

The target words in the left column have other meanings besides those used in earth science. Match each word with its correct, nonscientific meaning in the right column. Write the letter of your answer on the line before each word. Check your answers in a dictionary.

_____ 1. gorge   **a.** money put in a bank

_____ 2. avalanche   **b.** excitable

_____ 3. ridge   **c.** having brilliance, glowing

_____ 4. deposit   **d.** in levels or ranks, like classes of society

_____ 5. oasis   **e.** the narrow passage down which food goes; the throat

_____ 6. volcanic   **f.** a raised line or narrow strip

_____ 7. stratified   **g.** a sudden, overwhelming quantity of something

_____ 8. molten   **h.** any place offering relief from difficulty

---

Wordsmart: Etymology

The words for many natural formations were inspired by their physical qualities. Powerful fiery eruptions reminded the ancients of Vulcan, the Roman god of fire, so these eruptions came to be called *volcanoes*. The large holes in the sides of mountains are called *caverns*, from Latin word *cavus*, meaning "hollow."

LESSON 8 Words About the Sea

Target Words

barge, *n.* a large flat-bottomed boat, usually used for carrying freight

berth, *n.* space for maneuvering or docking a ship; a sleeping space on a ship

cruise, *n., v.* a sea voyage for pleasure; to sail for pleasure

fathom, *n., v.* a length of six feet, used as a measurement of water depth; to measure the depth of

galley, *n.* the area of a ship where food is cooked

gusty, *adj.* having sudden short bursts of wind

harpoon, *n., v.* a spear with a line attached, used to kill big sea animals; to use this spear

jettison, *v.* to throw overboard

latitude, *n.* distance north or south of the equator, measured in degrees

marine, *adj.* having to do with the sea

navigate, *v.* to steer a ship or plan its course; to travel by water

scuba, *n.* equipment that divers wear to breathe underwater

GETTING STARTED

The **specialized vocabulary,** or specific group of words, that people use in talking about the sea may be unfamiliar to you. Whether you are reading a poem for an English class or an article for a geography lesson, you will find it helpful to know words that relate to the sea.

I. Practice the Words

EXERCISE 1: Solve a Paragraph Puzzle

Using the target words and your knowledge of paragraph clues, fill in all the blank spaces below. Use each word only once. Be sure the words fit grammatically into the sentences.

On Saturday, our ship pulled out of its _____ and left on a

_____. Besides the ports we would visit, we looked forward to the

entertainment on board and the tasty food prepared in the ship's _____. It

was exciting to leave from New England, where sailors once set out to _____

whales. Now there are no whaling boats, but we did have to _____ past several

ships. One was a _____ weighed down by so many tires that I wondered if the

crew would have to _____ some of them to make the ship lighter. As we passed

a small island, our captain asked the first mate to _____ the waters to make

sure they were deep enough to cross. Our ship was sailing far from the equator, in a northern

_____ where the winds can be _____. There would be no

_____ diving among the _____ animals in these cold waters.

UNIT 2

EXERCISE 2: Match Words to Context

Circle the letter of the choice that best completes each sentence.

1. He went to the ship's _____ to make breakfast.
   a. berth   **b.** galley   **c.** barge   **d.** latitude

2. To make more room, the people in the lifeboat had to _____ their belongings.
   a. fathom   **b.** navigate   **c.** jettison   **d.** harpoon

3. The divers checked their _____ gear before going underwater.
   a. galley   **b.** marine   **c.** scuba   **d.** latitude

4. The tugboat pulled a _____ loaded with oil drums.
   a. barge   **b.** galley   **c.** scuba   **d.** cruise

5. To determine how far north we were, the first mate measured our _____.
   a. fathom   **b.** harpoon   **c.** berth   **d.** latitude

6. The _____ wind rocked our sailboat from side to side.
   a. gusty   **b.** galley   **c.** scuba   **d.** cruise

7. The study of sea life is called _____ biology.
   a. gusty   **b.** scuba   **c.** latitude   **d.** marine

8. The wealthy couple planned to _____ the Mediterranean Sea on their yacht.
   a. cruise   **b.** jettison   **c.** harpoon   **d.** fathom

9. The captain found it tricky to _____ through the narrow passage.
   a. fathom   **b.** navigate   **c.** harpoon   **d.** jettison

10. Captain Ahab threw a _____ into the whale called Moby-Dick.
   a. marine   **b.** fathom   **c.** cruise   **d.** harpoon

11. The sunken rowboat lay one _____ beneath the surface of the water.
   a. marine   **b.** latitude   **c.** fathom   **d.** galley

12. The sailor rolled into his _____ with a huge yawn.
   a. barge   **b.** berth   **c.** harpoon   **d.** cruise

EXERCISE 3: Use Target Words in Writing

On a separate sheet of paper, write a sentence for each of the target words listed at the beginning of this lesson. Be sure your sentences show that you understand what the words mean.

EXAMPLE **berth**   *The berth was so short that the sailor could not stretch his legs at night.*

EXERCISE 4: Match Ideas

On the line before each item, write the target word that is most clearly related to the situation described in the sentence. You will not use all the target words.

_____ **1.** The ship is heavy, so the crew needs to toss some freight overboard.

_____ **2.** The captain calculates how far south the ship is from the equator.

_____ **3.** The captain must determine if the water is deep enough to sail in.

_____ **4.** The crew uses a weapon to kill the whale for its oil and other products.

_____ **5.** Sudden bursts of wind disturb what had earlier been a calm sea.

_____ **6.** Vacationers are traveling to a tropical island.

_____ **7.** Divers search for sunken ships carrying valuable cargo.

_____ **8.** The boat was loaded with garbage and towed out to sea.

_____ **9.** All the captain's skill is required to enter the harbor in a storm.

_____ **10.** They are studying 16 types of seaweed at the Ocean Institute.

EXERCISE 5: Determine True/False

On the line before each statement, write *T* if the statement is true. Write *F* if it is false. Use your knowledge of the boldfaced target words to help you decide. Refer to the definitions in the target word list if necessary.

_____ **1.** If a ship is sinking, the crew might **jettison** the heaviest cargo.

_____ **2.** You measure **latitude** to see how far west a ship is from the California coast.

_____ **3.** You are likely to find pots and pans in a ship's **galley**.

_____ **4.** Three **fathoms** equals eighteen feet.

_____ **5.** A diver can use **scuba** gear to breathe underwater.

_____ **6.** A whale probably enjoys the feeling of a **harpoon**.

_____ **7.** You are likely to find a blanket and pillow in a sailor's **berth.**

_____ **8.** **Gusty** winds can create high waves on the ocean.

_____ **9.** The desert is a good place to look for **marine** animals.

_____ **10.** Most vacationers would rather travel on a yacht than a **barge**.

_____ **11.** A good sailor knows how to **navigate** through narrow channels.

_____ **12.** If you have to get somewhere quickly, you should **cruise** to your destination.

EXERCISE 6: Speaking

Discuss one of the following topics with a small group of your classmates. Use at least two target words in your discussion.

1. Discuss with classmates a book you read or a movie you saw that was about the sea.

2. Describe to classmates a trip involving the sea that you might consider taking in the future.

II. Vocabulary Challenge

EXERCISE 7: Word Play

Unscramble each cluster of scrambled letters to form a different target word. Write the target words on the lines provided. Use the clues in parentheses to help you figure out the target words.

1. sytug   _____ (it's what winds might be)

2. tedaliut   _____ (it's measured in degrees)

3. bucas   _____ (divers use it)

4. phooran   _____ (whalers throw it)

5. snejtoit   _____ (antonym of *keep*)

6. aateving   _____ (to guide or steer)

7. yelagl   _____ (a ship's kitchen)

8. trehb   _____ (a ship's bed)

9. tamhof   _____ (six feet underwater)

10. sucier   _____ (type of vacation)

11. nimera   _____ (describing the sea)

12. gbear   _____ (a tugboat often pulls it)

Wordsmart: Etymology

The word *scuba,* first recorded in 1952, is an acronym for "**s**elf-**c**ontained **u**nderwater **b**reathing **a**pparatus." An acronym is a word formed from the first letters of other words. *Scuba* has become so widely used that people don't think of it as an acronym and use it to form other words, such as *scuba-dive.* In fact, a verb *scuba* was first recorded in 1973 and is still in use.

Check Your Knowledge: Unit 2

By now you have added 48 new words to your word bank. Test your ability to use these words in the following exercises.

A. Use Context Clues

On the line before each sentence, write the letter of the word or phrase that is closest in meaning to the boldfaced target word. Use the context clues to help you decide.

_____ **1.** The flooding in the town was **predictable** after the heavy rainfall.
    a. puzzling   **b.** expected   **c.** welcome   **d.** invisible

_____ **2.** When Stan had trouble with his homework, Stella **immediately** offered to help.
    a. slowly   **b.** promptly   **c.** with hope   **d.** with regret

_____ **3.** Emma often daydreams in class, forgetting the **reality** of student life.
    a. beauty   **b.** difficulty   **c.** ease   **d.** truth

_____ **4.** The first mate helped the captain **navigate** the ship through a narrow channel.
    a. steer   **b.** keep clean   **c.** carry cargo   **d.** measure

_____ **5.** Did the child receive a **punishment** for misbehaving?
    a. penalty   **b.** command   **c.** reward   **d.** reaction

_____ **6.** My sister studied horseshoe crabs and other **marine** life in her biology class.
    a. human   **b.** scientific   **c.** of the sea   **d.** of the past

_____ **7.** We went down to the **galley** to cook a meal.
    a. hallway   **b.** captain's table   **c.** ship's kitchen   **d.** fireplace

_____ **8.** Dad gets **sentimental** when he hears rock music from the past.
    a. angry   **b.** emotional   **c.** nervous   **d.** confused

_____ **9.** My **berth** on the ship was a comfortable spot to spend the night.
    a. closet   **b.** deck chair   **c.** ship's deck   **d.** ship's bed

_____ **10.** The roller coaster is the main **attraction** at the amusement park.
    a. surprise   **b.** disappointment   **c.** industry   **d.** interest

B. Identify Antonyms

Write the letter of the word that is most nearly the opposite of the boldfaced target word.

_____ **1. accidental**   **a.** planned   **b.** sudden   **c.** careless   **d.** casual

_____ **2. flexible**   **a.** stubborn   **b.** weak   **c.** agreeable   **d.** foolish

_____ **3. heroic**   **a.** brave   **b.** unknown   **c.** cowardly   **d.** uneducated

_____ **4. restless**   **a.** generous   **b.** calm   **c.** confused   **d.** sleepy

_____ **5. thoughtless**   **a.** unwise   **b.** unspoken   **c.** active   **d.** considerate

_____ **6. jettison**   **a.** destroy   **b.** discard   **c.** hide   **d.** keep

C. Match Synonyms

Write the letter of the word that is closest in meaning to the boldfaced target word.

_____ **1. amazement**   **a.** respect   **b.** hope   **c.** fear   **d.** wonder

_____ **2. competition**   **a.** anger   **b.** admiration   **c.** rivalry   **d.** activity

_____ **3. limitation**   **a.** freedom   **b.** obedience   **c.** confusion   **d.** boundary

_____ **4. sorrowful**   **a.** sad   **b.** charming   **c.** joyful   **d.** dull

_____ **5. journalist**   **a.** speaker   **b.** reporter   **c.** teacher   **d.** actor

_____ **6. gorge**   **a.** hill   **b.** peak   **c.** canyon   **d.** scenery

_____ **7. ridge**   **a.** crest   **b.** cave   **c.** wilderness   **d.** desert

_____ **8. stratified**   **a.** smooth   **b.** layered   **c.** rocky   **d.** equal

_____ **9. gusty**   **a.** windy   **b.** confusing   **c.** healthy   **d.** salty

_____ **10. loyalty**   **a.** weakness   **b.** betrayal   **c.** strength   **d.** devotion

D. Match Ideas

On the line before each item, write the target word from the list below that is most clearly related to the situation described in the sentence.

| avalanche | cavern | harpoon | jettison | molten | oasis |

_____ **1.** We are trapped by snow coming down a hillside.

_____ **2.** We are lost in a large hollow area underneath the rocks.

_____ **3.** We flee from the hot liquefied rock pouring out of a volcano.

_____ **4.** We use a large spear to hunt whales in the ocean.

_____ **5.** Parched with thirst, we long for a place with water in the desert.

E. Add Base Words

Match each base word below with an italic suffix. Use each base word only once. Write the new word you have formed and define it without using the base word in your definition.

| clock | counsel | excel | immediate | success |

1. -ence _____

meaning: _____

2. -ful _____

meaning: _____

3. -ly _____

meaning: _____

4. -or _____

meaning: _____

5. -wise _____

meaning: _____

F. Analyze Context and Meaning

Each of the following statements contains at least one boldfaced target word. On the line before the statement, write *T* if it is true. Write *F* if it is false.

_____ **1. Latitude** tells you how far a ship is from the equator.

_____ **2.** The **fathom** is a unit for measuring a ship's **latitude**.

_____ **3. Scuba** gear can help you breathe underwater.

_____ **4.** An **outcrop** is a **deposit** of a mineral below the soil.

_____ **5. Carbon** and **sulfur** are both chemical elements found in nature.

_____ **6.** A **volcanic disturbance** may produce **molten** rock.

_____ **7. Clockwise** is the direction in which the hands of a clock move.

_____ **8.** A **journalist** deals with facts and reality.

G. Use Words in Context

On the line before each sentence, write the target word that best completes the sentence. Use each target word only once. Some words will not be used.

barge	cruise	disturbance	explorer	historical
jettison	restless	thoughtless	volcanic	

_____ **1.** The _____ carried freight from a port in New Jersey up the river to Albany.

_____ **2.** Near the site of the eruption was a great deal of _____ ash.

_____ **3.** My aunt and uncle like to _____ the Caribbean Sea every winter.

_____ **4.** The _____ novel was set during World War II.

_____ **5.** Columbus was an Italian _____ who sailed under the Spanish flag.

_____ **6.** The _____ outside woke me from a sound sleep.

Feature: Denotation and Connotation

UNIT 3

WHAT IS IT?

A word's **denotation** is its dictionary definition. Its **connotation** includes the feelings and ideas that the word expresses beyond the dictionary definition. For example, the words *slender*, *thin*, and *skinny* all have the same denotation—they all mean "having little fat." However, the words have different shades of meaning ranging from positive to neutral to negative.

> **Positive connotation:** Running for the track team has made Alan **slender.**
> **Neutral connotation:** Running for the track team has made Alan **thin.**
> **Negative connotation:** Running for the track team has made Alan **skinny.**

WHY IT MATTERS

Skilled writers know all about words and their shades of meaning. They are experts at selecting just the right words to convey their ideas. Learning the different connotations of synonyms can help you become a more accurate writer as well as a better reader.

EXERCISE 1: Identify Positive and Negative Connotations

For each phrase below, decide whether the boldfaced synonym has a positive or a negative connotation. Put a plus sign (+) on the line after the phrase to show a positive connotation. Put a minus sign (−) on the line to show a negative connotation.

1. a strong **stink** _____

   a strong **fragrance** _____

2. a **commanding** leader _____

   a **bossy** leader _____

3. a **reckless** plan _____

   a **daring** plan _____

4. a **casual** appearance _____

   a **messy** appearance _____

5. **gossiped** for hours _____

   chatted for hours _____

6. a **thrifty** old man _____

   a **stingy** old man _____

7. a **strict** teacher _____

   a **harsh** teacher _____

8. a **snobbish** leader _____

   a **dignified** leader _____

9. a **lively** child _____

   a **rowdy** child _____

10. an **easygoing** friend _____

    a **lazy** friend _____

EXERCISE 2: Use Words with Positive and Negative Connotations

In the first paragraph below, circle the words that have a positive connotation. In the second paragraph, circle the words that have a negative connotation. Use a dictionary or thesaurus if needed.

Positive connotations: Although she has been at Valley Middle School for almost twenty years, Ms. Baxter is a very (youthful, immature) teacher. Her students admire her because she holds (hostile, strong) opinions on many different subjects. She is not afraid to try (creative, weird) teaching methods that will help her students understand new ideas. She is a real (leader, dictator) in the classroom.

Negative connotations: I was surprised to get a birthday gift from my Aunt Joanna. She is a (curious, nosy) person, so she had asked my relatives what I might like. I tore the (colorful, gaudy) paper off the package and found a(n) (cheap, inexpensive) shirt made of (flimsy, delicate) material. It was covered with (detailed, fussy) embroidery and (eye-catching, flashy) sequins. It was a very (strange, unique) piece of clothing.

EXERCISE 3: Make Words Your Own

For each neutral word in the left column, write at least one synonym with a positive connotation and one with a negative connotation. If necessary, use a dictionary or a thesaurus to help you. The first one has been completed for you.

Neutral	Positive	Negative
odor (n.)	fragrance, aroma	stink, smell
1. active (adj.)		
2. usual (adj.)		
3. weak (adj.)		
4. simple (adj.)		
5. walk (v.)		
6. plain (adj.)		
7. sing (v.)		
8. hard (adj.)		

LESSON 9 **Latin Roots and Related Words I**

Target Words	Root	Meaning
intermission, *n.*	*miss/mit*	to send
permission, *n.*		
submit, *v.*		
transmit, *v.*		
importance, *n.*	*port*	to carry
portable, *adj.*		
transport, *v.*		
transportation, *n.*		
description, *n.*	*scrib/script*	to write
prescribe, *v.*		
scribble, *v.*		
subscription, *n.*		

GETTING STARTED

Unlike base words, **roots** are word parts that cannot stand alone. A group of words that share the same root is called a **word family.** Roots must be combined with prefixes and suffixes to form words. In this lesson, you will learn the roots *miss/mit, port,* and *scrib/script* from Latin—the language of ancient Rome. You will need to use your knowledge of the prefixes you learned in Unit 1 to help you understand the target words in this lesson. The cluster below shows a word family built around the root *scrib/script.*

I. Practice the Words

EXERCISE 1: Understand Latin Roots

Circle the root in each target word. Then think of two more words that have the same root.

1. submit   word 1: _____   word 2: _____

2. portable   word 1: _____   word 2: _____

3. scribble   word 1: _____   word 2: _____

EXERCISE 2: Identify Roots and Meanings

Underline the root in each target word on the left. Then match each word with its correct meaning on the right. Write the letter of the correct meaning in the space provided. Use each meaning only once.

1. intermission _____

a. to carry people or goods from one place to another

2. permission _____

b. able to be carried

3. submit _____

c. a system or vehicle for carrying people or goods from one place to another

4. transmit _____

d. consent; approval

5. importance _____

e. a signed agreement to receive magazines, newspapers, performance tickets, or services for a certain period of time

6. portable _____

f. to send from one person or place to another; to send a signal, as by wire or radio

7. transport _____

g. a break between parts of a theatrical or musical performance; a pause

8. transportation _____

h. to present for review or decision; to surrender

9. description _____

i. to write hastily in a way that is hard to read

10. prescribe _____

j. something that gives written or spoken details

11. scribble _____

k. to set down as a rule; to order the use of (a medicine)

12. subscription _____

l. significance; influence

EXERCISE 3: Analyze Context and Meaning

On the line before each statement, write *T* if the statement is true. Write *F* if it is false. Use your knowledge of the boldfaced target words to help you decide.

_____ **1.** A laptop computer is more **portable** than a desktop.

_____ **2.** Freight trains are one way to **transport** goods across the country.

_____ **3.** An **intermission** usually occurs at the beginning of a play.

_____ **4.** A doctor might **prescribe** bed rest rather than medicine to treat a cold.

_____ **5.** If you **scribble**, your handwriting will be easy to read.

_____ **6.** Your magazines are delivered regularly when you buy a **subscription**.

EXERCISE 4: Use Words in Context

Using your knowledge of context clues such as cause and effect, restatement, and example, select a target word from the list to complete each sentence and write it on the line provided. Use each word only once.

| description | importance | intermission | permission | portable | prescribe |
| scribble | submit | subscription | transmit | transport | transportation |

1. Since her skin was dry and itchy, she asked her doctor to _____ a cream.

2. The witness gave the police a detailed _____ of the thief, including his height, weight, and age.

3. Jan's parents gave her a one-year _____ to a teen magazine.

4. The council will _____, or propose, plans for a new library to the mayor for his review.

5. Anton's _____ music player was so lightweight that he carried it in his pocket wherever he went.

6. The concert was two hours long, so we got up to stretch our legs during

   the _____.

7. Planes, trains, cars, and ships are all forms of _____.

8. After much discussion, Helen's parents gave her _____ to attend the party.

9. Many people use computers to _____ electronic messages.

10. Jason used to _____, but now his handwriting is easy to read.

11. Does the factory _____, or carry, its goods across the country by rail or by truck?

12. You might think that it doesn't matter what you eat, but health officials stress the

    _____ of a balanced diet.

Exercise 5: Identify Synonyms and Antonyms

In each item below, a boldfaced target word is paired with another word. On the line before each pair, write *S* if the two words are synonyms. Write *A* if they are antonyms.

_____ **1. submit**/ receive   _____ **5. transmit**/ send

_____ **2. permission**/ refusal   _____ **6. portable**/ fixed

_____ **3. prescribe**/ order   _____ **7. scribble**/ scrawl

_____ **4. transport**/ carry   _____ **8. importance**/ insignificance

EXERCISE 6: Use Target Words in Writing

On a separate sheet of paper, write a paragraph about how you use the Internet for schoolwork or recreation. Use at least three target words in your paragraph.

II. Vocabulary Challenge

EXERCISE 7: Extend Your Vocabulary

Fill in this word cluster with six words that contain the Latin root *audi*. Write the definition of each word on the blank lines below. Your definitions should reflect the meaning of the root *audi*. Check your answers in a dictionary.

audi: "to hear"

1. word: _____

   meaning: _____

2. word: _____

   meaning: _____

3. word: _____

   meaning: _____

4. word: _____

   meaning: _____

5. word: _____

   meaning: _____

6. word: _____

   meaning: _____

Wordsmart: Etymology

Before printing was invented, books had to be written by hand. The person who wrote them down was called a *scribe,* and the handwritten book was called a *manuscript*—a word that joins the root *scrib/script* to another Latin root, *man,* meaning "hand." Today, a manuscript is usually typed on a computer, but the word still refers to the version a writer works hard to produce, before the book is printed and distributed.

UNIT 3

LESSON 10 Words Used in Math

Target Words

decimal, *n.* a number that is smaller than a whole number expressed with a decimal point. For example, 0.7 represents 7 tenths, or 7/10.

denominator, *n.* the number below the fraction bar in a fraction that tells how many parts the whole is divided into.

equation, *n.* a mathematical sentence formed by placing an equal sign (=) between two expressions. For example, 3 + 4 = 7 is an equation.

factor, *n.* a number in a mathematical expression that is multiplied or divided by another number. In the equation 2 x 3 = 6, the numbers 2 and 3 are factors of 6.

fraction, *n.* a number of the form *a/b* used to describe parts of a whole. A fraction has two parts: a numerator and a denominator.

integer, *n.* any whole number, including negative numbers and zero.

negative, *adj.* referring to numbers that are less than zero.

percent, *n.* one part in a hundred. *Percent* means "per hundred," or "out of 100." The symbol for percent is %.

positive, *adj.* referring to numbers that are greater than zero

proportion, *n.* an equation that shows that two ratios have the same value. For example, 1/2 = 3/6 is a proportion.

rate, *n.* an amount measured in relation to each unit of something else, often expressed with a slash (/), as in 55 miles/hour.

ratio, *n.* a relationship between two numbers. For example, *the ratio of teachers to students is 1 : 15* means there is one teacher for every 15 students.

GETTING STARTED

Mathematics has its own specialized vocabulary. Some of the words in math are represented by symbols such as the plus sign (+) and the equal sign (=). Other words, such as *factor* and *negative,* have a different, more precise, meaning in mathematics than they do in everyday usage. The terms and symbols in this lesson will help you master the special vocabulary of math.

I. Practice the Words

EXERCISE 1: Understand Words Used in Math

Identify two target words that are familiar to you. Use each word in a sentence.

1. word: _____

   sentence: _____

2. word: _____

   sentence: _____

EXERCISE 2: Match Words to Symbols

Circle the letter of the target word that best identifies the example in the left column.

1. −3　　　　　　**a.** positive number　　**b.** negative number　　**c.** product　　**d.** fraction

2. 0　　　　　　　**a.** positive number　　**b.** negative number　　**c.** integer　　**d.** rate

3. 8 + 2 = 10　　**a.** equation　　　　　**b.** denominator　　　**c.** ratio　　　**d.** factor

4. 2.11　　　　　**a.** percent　　　　　　**b.** decimal　　　　　**c.** factor　　**d.** denominator

5. 1 : 7　　　　　**a.** fraction　　　　　　**b.** equation　　　　　**c.** decimal　　**d.** ratio

6. 3/5　　　　　　**a.** integer　　　　　　**b.** denominator　　　**c.** equation　　**d.** fraction

7. $100/ticket　　**a.** decimal　　　　　**b.** equation　　　　　**c.** rate　　　**d.** percent

8. 60%　　　　　 **a.** percent　　　　　　**b.** proportion　　　　**c.** decimal　　**d.** integer

EXERCISE 3: Match Words to Context

Circle the letter of the target word that best completes each sentence.

1. A number that is greater than 0 is
   a. positive.　　　　**b.** negative.　　　　**c.** a decimal.　　　　**d.** a rate.

2. Each of the numbers −67, 0, 1, and 254 is
   a. a percent.　　　 **b.** an integer.　　　 **c.** a rate.　　　　　**d.** a proportion.

3. The number sentence 6 − 1 = 5 is
   a. a fraction.　　　**b.** an equation.　　　**c.** a ratio.　　　　　**d.** an integer.

4. In the number sentence 3 x 8 = 24, 8 is a
   a. denominator.　　**b.** decimal.　　　　　**c.** proportion.　　　　**d.** factor.

5. The equation 5/20 = 1/4 is a
   a. rate.　　　　　　**b.** fraction.　　　　　**c.** proportion.　　　　**d.** factor.

6. The expression 3 : 1 is a
   a. rate.　　　　　　**b.** decimal.　　　　　**c.** ratio.　　　　　　**d.** percent.

7. In the number 7/8, 8 is the
   a. fraction.　　　　**b.** rate.　　　　　　**c.** ratio.　　　　　　**d.** denominator.

8. 60 miles/1 hour expresses a
   a. percent.　　　　**b.** factor.　　　　　**c.** rate.　　　　　　**d.** proportion.

EXERCISE 4: Analyze Context and Meaning

On the line before each statement, write *T* if the statement is true. Write *F* if it is false. Use your knowledge of the boldfaced target words to help you decide.

_____ **1.** A **proportion** shows that two ratios are equivalent.

_____ **2.** If you add a **positive** number to a **negative** number, you always get zero.

_____ **3.** Zero is an **integer,** but it is not a **positive** number.

_____ **4.** In the **equation** 7 x 100 = 700, the number 700 is a **factor.**

_____ **5.** In the **fraction** 3/8, the **denominator** is 3.

_____ **6.** The **decimal** 2.1 means the same as the **fraction** 2 1/10.

_____ **7.** The expression 75% is not a **percent.**

_____ **8.** The number 3 is a **factor** of the number 20.

_____ **9.** The **fraction** 33/100 is equal to 33 **percent.**

_____ **10.** The expression 6 : 7 is not a **ratio.**

_____ **11.** If a train is traveling 60 miles per hour, its **rate** may be written as 60 miles/1 hour.

_____ **12.** In an **equation,** two mathematical expressions are seen as unequal.

_____ **13.** A **percent,** a **rate,** and a **fraction** all express a relationship of one number to another.

_____ **14.** In the number 7.75, the **denominator** is 5.

EXERCISE 5: Use Target Words in Writing

On a separate sheet of paper, write a paragraph about an exciting competition, such as a track meet or a school election, that you have participated in or seen. Use at least three target words to describe the competitors, the viewers, and the results of the contest. A sample sentence has been given to help you.

EXAMPLE   **percent**   *The number of games our team won was 10 percent below that of the other team.*

UNIT 3

UNIT 3

EXERCISE 6: Speaking

Discuss one of the following topics with a small group of your classmates.

1. Explain the difference between a fraction and a decimal. In addition to the words *fraction* and *decimal,* use at least one more target word.

2. Give details about a purchase that you or someone else made. Use at least two target words.

3. Explain what an integer is. In addition to the word *integer,* use at least two more target words.

II. Vocabulary Challenge

EXERCISE 7: Word Search

Find and circle each target word hidden in this maze. The words may appear horizontally, vertically, or diagonally. They may be written forward or backward. Different words may overlap and use the same letter.

```
N E F R A C T I O N N
F A C T O R E N I O E
P M E K W N U T T I G
N U M Y R F Q E A T A
L O D E T I A G R A T
L A P E T A R E Z U I
A J E C R D P R W Q V
M N E V R A C T J E E
I P R O P O R T I O N
C E V I T I S O P N O
E T N E C R E P R Y W
D E N O M I N A T O R
```

WORD LIST

decimal
denominator
equation
factor
fraction
integer
negative
percent
positive
proportion
rate
ratio

Wordsmart: Etymology

A *percent,* which shows the portion of every hundred, contains the Latin root *cent,* which means "hundred." The root occurs in several other English words—a *century* is a hundred years, for example, and a *centipede* is an insect that looks like it has a hundred feet. We even call our unit for a hundredth of a dollar a *cent.*

LESSON 11 Latin Roots and Related Words II

Target Words	Roots	Meaning
refer, *v.*	*fer*	to bear; to carry
reference, *n.*		
transfer, *v.*		
conform, *v.*	*form*	to form; to shape
inform, *v.*		
reformer, *n.*		
transformation, *n.*		
extend, *v.*	*tend/tens/tent*	to stretch
extension, *n.*		
intention, *n.*		
contract, *v.*	*tract*	to pull; to drag
extract, *v.*		

GETTING STARTED

Remember that a **word family** is a group of words that share the same **root**—a word part that cannot stand alone. For example, the target words *contract* and *extract* share the root *tract*. The cluster below shows other words that contain the root *tract*. What do each of these words have to do with dragging or pulling?

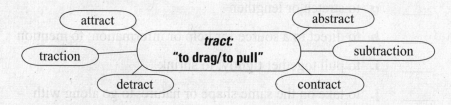

attract   abstract
traction   *tract:* "to drag/ to pull"   subtraction
detract   contract

The target words in this lesson also include prefixes, which you will need to know in order to define the target words.

Prefix	Meaning	Prefix	Meaning
re-	again; backward	*ex-*	away from; past
con-	with; together	*trans-*	across; through
in-	in; toward		

I. Practice the Words

EXERCISE 1: Understand Latin Roots

Circle the root in each target word and provide two other words that have the same root.
Do not use target words.

1. **transfer**   word 1: _____   word 2: _____

2. **conform**   word 1: _____   word 2: _____

3. **extension**   word 1: _____   word 2: _____

EXERCISE 2: Identify Roots and Meanings

Underline the root in each target word on the left. Then match each word with its correct
meaning on the right. Write the letter of the correct meaning in the space provided. Use
each meaning only once.

1. conform   _____   **a.** to pull out

2. contract   _____   **b.** to shape the mind by teaching or training; to make others
                                            aware of something

3. extend   _____   **c.** a mention of an occurrence or situation; a mark or note
                                            that directs a reader to another source

4. extension   _____   **d.** someone who tries to reshape or change things

5. extract   _____   **e.** a noticeable change in appearance or character

6. inform   _____   **f.** to carry or send something from one person or place
                                            to another

7. intention   _____   **g.** to stretch or lengthen

8. refer   _____   **h.** to direct to a source for help or information; to mention

9. reference   _____   **i.** to pull together tightly; to shrink

10. reformer   _____   **j.** to take on the same shape or nature; to go along with

11. transfer   _____   **k.** a purpose; an aim that guides one's actions

12. transformation   _____   **l.** an addition; an allowance of extra time

EXERCISE 3: Analyze Context and Meaning

On the line before each statement, write *T* if the statement is true. Write *F* if it is false. Use your knowledge of the boldfaced target words to help you decide.

_____ **1.** If Gillian undergoes a **transformation**, she is the same now as she was before.

_____ **2.** A **reformer** tries to improve society.

_____ **3.** You ask for an **extension** on your term paper when you turn it in on time.

_____ **4.** If your **intention** is to graduate, you have to stay in school.

_____ **5.** A science paper might contain a **reference** to the research of others.

_____ **6.** If you **inform** others about a new schedule, you fail to mention it.

_____ **7.** People **conform** when they want to fit in with a group.

_____ **8.** A gardener should **extract** tree roots that are strong and healthy.

EXERCISE 4: Use Synonyms in Context

On the line after each sentence, write the target word with a similar meaning to the boldfaced word. Use each target word only once.

1. City officials built an **addition** onto the public library. _____

2. To get home, Sharon needs to **switch** to another bus. _____

3. The dentist had to **pull** a tooth from Stan's mouth. _____

4. The airplane brought a great **change** in the way people travel. _____

5. **Tighten** your stomach muscles when you do this exercise. _____

6. Of which famous poem did your paper include a **mention?** _____

7. I entered the store with the **goal** of buying a new pair of shoes. _____

8. Do not change your thinking just to **agree** with your friends. _____

9. Please **tell** Roberta of the change in plans. _____

10. Jane Addams was an **activist** who improved the lives of poor people. _____

11. The manager planned to **lengthen** store hours for the sale. _____

12. Family doctors sometimes **direct** their patients to specialists. _____

EXERCISE 5: Use Target Words in Writing

On a separate sheet of paper, write a paragraph about someone who changed the world for the better. It could be someone famous or someone you know. Use at least four target words in your paragraph.

EXERCISE 6: Identify Antonyms

On the line before each item, write the letter of the word that is most nearly the opposite of the boldfaced target word.

_____	1. **conform**	**a.** agree	**b.** shape	**c.** relate	**d.** rebel
_____	2. **contract**	**a.** expand	**b.** expect	**c.** disturb	**d.** shrink
_____	3. **extend**	**a.** shorten	**b.** lengthen	**c.** rebuild	**d.** remark
_____	4. **extract**	**a.** shorten	**b.** destroy	**c.** insert	**d.** insult
_____	5. **inform**	**a.** tell	**b.** shape	**c.** withhold	**d.** share
_____	6. **refer**	**a.** direct	**b.** ignore	**c.** visit	**d.** assist
_____	7. **transfer**	**a.** move	**b.** excite	**c.** travel	**d.** remain
_____	8. **transformation**	**a.** purpose	**b.** sameness	**c.** change	**d.** mention

II. Vocabulary Challenge

EXERCISE 7: Extend Your Vocabulary

The incomplete words below have the same roots as the target words. Use the clues to help you complete those words, and write the missing letters on the lines.

EXAMPLE a meeting where people share ideas C O N F E R E N C E

1. to like one thing more than another _ _ _ F E R

2. a piece of farm equipment that pulls things T R A C T _ _ _

3. to redo in a better form; to improve _ _ F O R M

4. pulled tight physically or emotionally T E N S _

5. special clothes worn by members of a certain group _ _ _ F O R M

6. to take away _ _ T R A C T

7. casual and relaxed _ _ F O R M _ _

8. to plan to do something _ _ T E N D

9. to pull one's attention to something else _ _ T R A C T

10. able to produce fruit, seeds, or offspring F E R _ _ _ _

Wordsmart: Usage

Some words use suffixes to change from a verb to a noun: *extend/extension, refer/reference*. In other cases, the same word is used as both a noun and a verb: *contract, extract, transfer*. A *transfer,* for example, is not only a verb that means "to pass from one person, place, or thing to another"; it is also a noun that means "a ticket that allows a passenger to change from one form of public transportation to another as part of one trip," such as a bus *transfer.*

LESSON 12 Words for Measurements and Shapes

Target Words
adjacent, *adj.* sharing a border or endpoint
area, *n.* the amount of surface covered by a figure; area is expressed in square units such as square miles or square feet
circumference, *n.* the distance around a circle
complementary, *adj.* referring to two angles whose measures have a sum of 90 degrees
cylinder, *n.* a solid figure with circles at either end, shaped like a roll of wrapping paper or a soup can
diameter, *n.* the distance across a circle through its center
isosceles, *adj.* a triangle in which two of the three sides are equal in length
parallel, *adj.* referring to lines in the same plane that are always the same distance apart and never meet
perimeter, *n.* the distance around a figure, measured in linear units
perpendicular, *adj.* referring to two lines that cross each other at a right angle (90 degrees)
polygon, *n.* a closed figure formed by three or more segments called sides
volume, *n.* the amount of space occupied by a solid figure, expressed in cubic units

GETTING STARTED

The special terms for measurements and shapes are important to mathematics, engineering, and many other fields. The terms also come up in everyday situations—like describing an object, for example, or repairing something in your home. In this lesson, you will learn several important terms for measurements and shapes.

I. Practice the Words

EXERCISE 1: Solve a Sentence Puzzle

For each choice in parentheses, circle the word that best completes the sentence.

1. The farmer had to fence in a cornfield, so he measured its (volume, perimeter).

2. The (diameter, volume) of the circle was 3 inches.

3. We measured the (area, diameter) of the eight-sided (cylinder, polygon).

4. (Parallel, Perpendicular) lines cannot form a right angle.

5. Main Street meets Oak Street at a (complementary, perpendicular) angle.

6. The community garden plots are (isosceles, adjacent) to each other.

EXERCISE 2: Analyze Context and Meaning

On the line before each statement, write *T* if the statement is true. Write *F* if it is false. Use your knowledge of the boldfaced target words to help you decide.

_____ 1. **Perpendicular** lines are sometimes **parallel**.

_____ 2. The amount of space inside a **cylinder** is called its **volume**.

_____ 3. The three sides of an **isosceles** triangle might measure 2, 3, and 4 inches.

_____ 4. The **circumference** of a circle is greater than its **diameter**.

_____ 5. An **isosceles** triangle is a kind of **polygon**.

_____ 6. **Parallel** lines form **complementary** angles.

_____ 7. The **diameter** of a square joins two opposite corners.

_____ 8. The letter H has two **parallel** lines connected by a line that is **perpendicular** to them.

_____ 9. The **area** of a circle depends upon its ratio.

_____ 10. The **perimeter** of a square can be determined if you measure one side.

EXERCISE 3: Identify Synonyms

Circle the letter of the word that is closest in meaning to the boldfaced target word.

1. **adjacent**	a. touching	b. parallel	c. complementary	d. distant
2. **cylinder**	a. can	b. box	c. ball	d. cone
3. **perpendicular**	a. parallel	b. crossing	c. near	d. isosceles
4. **area**	a. length	b. diameter	c. square footage	d. perimeter
5. **volume**	a. shape	b. length	c. width	d. capacity
6. **polygon**	a. circle	b. figure	c. circumference	d. cylinder
7. **complementary**	a. mutual	b. isosceles	c. free	d. favorable
8. **perimeter**	a. cylinder	b. diameter	c. boundary	d. width

EXERCISE 4: Use Target Words in Writing

On a separate sheet of paper, write a sentence for each of the target words listed at the beginning of this lesson. Be sure your sentences show that you understand what the words mean.

EXAMPLE   **cylinder**   *The tube had the shape of a cylinder.*

EXERCISE 5: Match Ideas to Context

Using your knowledge of sentence clues, circle the letter of the answer that best completes each sentence.

1. A **polygon** is a figure that
   a. has only two sides.
   b. has many sides and angles.
   c. is a circle.
   d. looks like a cylinder.

2. The **circumference** of a circle is the
   a. distance around it.
   b. area inside it.
   c. length of a line through its center.
   d. sum of its angles.

3. The **adjacent** sides of a figure
   a. touch each other.
   b. are opposite each other.
   c. have the same length.
   d. cross each other.

4. **Complementary** angles total
   a. 45 degrees.
   b. 90 degrees.
   c. 180 degrees.
   d. 360 degrees.

5. Lines that are **perpendicular** form a
   a. 45-degree angle.
   b. triangle.
   c. cylinder.
   d. 90-degree angle.

6. To find the **perimeter** of a schoolyard you need to measure the
   a. right side.
   b. left side.
   c. outer edges.
   d. interior space.

7. A **cylinder** is shaped like a
   a. cube of ice.
   b. soccer ball.
   c. can of soup.
   d. pyramid.

8. The sides of an **isosceles** triangle might measure
   a. 3 inches, 4 inches, and 5 inches.
   b. 4 inches, 4 inches, and 4 inches.
   c. 4 inches, 5 inches, and 7 inches
   d. 3 inches, 3 inches, and 5 inches.

9. To measure the **area** of a room, first you measure its
   a. opposite angles.
   b. length and width.
   c. length from end to end.
   d. height from floor to ceiling.

10. Measuring the **volume** of a box tells you the
    a. length of the longest side.
    b. length of the shortest side.
    c. amount of space inside.
    d. number of angles it has.

11. **Parallel** lines
    a. never meet.
    b. cross each other twice.
    c. cross each other only once.
    d. form a right angle.

12. The **diameter** of a circle is the
    a. distance across the circle through its center.
    b. amount of space the circle occupies.
    c. area outside of the circle.
    d. shortest distance between two points.

EXERCISE 6: Speaking

Discuss one of the following topics with a small group of your classmates.

1. Describe a circle using at least two of the target words.

2. Describe a polygon of more than three sides. In addition to *polygon*, use at least two more target words.

II. Vocabulary Challenge

EXERCISE 7: Word Play

Match the terms on the right to the pictures on the left. Write the letter of the correct term on the line after each picture. Use each term only once.

1. _____   **a.** cylinder

2. _____   **b.** parallel lines

3. _____   **c.** polygon

4. _____   **d.** perpendicular lines

5. _____   **e.** circumference

6. _____   **f.** isosceles triangle

7. _____   **g.** complementary angles

8. _____   **h.** diameter

Wordsmart: Etymology

Polygon contains the prefix *poly*, which is the Greek word for "many." A *polysyllabic* word is one with several syllables, and a *polytechnic* school provides instruction in many technical subjects. Even the area in the Pacific known as *Polynesia* received its name because it has many islands. (The Greek word *nesos* means "island.")

Check Your Knowledge: Unit 3

By now you have added 48 new words to your vocabulary. Test your ability to use these words in the following exercises.

A. Determine Meaning from Context

On the line before each sentence, write the letter of the word or phrase that is closest in meaning to the boldfaced target word. Use the context clues to help you decide.

_____ **1.** Many people in New Orleans had no **intention** of moving, but the city was badly damaged by Hurricane Katrina.
   a. need　　　　**b.** agreement　　**c.** plan　　　　**d.** desire

_____ **2.** Do the lungs **contract** or expand when you breathe in?
   a. tighten　　　**b.** loosen　　　**c.** soften　　　**d.** harden

_____ **3.** After asking her several times, Alex received his mother's **permission** to attend summer camp.
   a. consent　　　**b.** speech　　　**c.** interest　　　**d.** warning

_____ **4.** One **polygon** had six sides; the other had eight.
   a. six-sided figure　**b.** triangle　　**c.** square　　　**d.** many-sided figure

_____ **5.** The Incas used peaceful and military means to **extend** their empire throughout western South America.
   a. hold　　　　**b.** stretch　　　**c.** withdraw　　**d.** protect

_____ **6.** Small-town radio stations often **transmit** weak signals that are hard to tune in.
   a. send　　　　**b.** create　　　**c.** prevent　　　**d.** receive

_____ **7.** The family stayed in two **adjacent** hotel rooms with a connecting door.
   a. large　　　　**b.** elegant　　　**c.** far apart　　**d.** adjoining

_____ **8.** Bella's letter from Italy included a **description** of Venice's canals and gondolas.
   a. map　　　　**b.** report　　　**c.** photograph　**d.** stamp

_____ **9.** The leader of a nation is a person of great **importance**.
   a. humor　　　**b.** confidence　**c.** power　　　**d.** intelligence

_____ **10.** The doctor had to **prescribe** a strong medicine to cure Stella's throat infection.
   a. mix　　　　**b.** study　　　**c.** test　　　　**d.** order

UNIT 3

B. Identify Synonyms

On the line before each item, write the letter of the word that is closest in meaning to the boldfaced target word.

_____ 1. **transformation**   a. stretch   b. activity   c. faith   d. change

_____ 2. **reference**   a. belief   b. mention   c. conclusion   d. fact

_____ 3. **inform**   a. carve   b. question   c. tell   d. lead

_____ 4. **intention**   a. worry   b. goal   c. schedule   d. mystery

_____ 5. **transfer**   a. shift   b. merge   c. ride   d. relax

_____ 6. **equation**   a. meaning   b. size   c. equality   d. failure

_____ 7. **intermission**   a. denial   b. purpose   c. reaction   d. break

_____ 8. **scribble**   a. create   b. scrawl   c. defeat   d. destroy

C. Identify Antonyms

On the line before each item, write the letter of the word that is most nearly the opposite of the boldfaced target word.

_____ 1. **conform**   a. support   b. rebel   c. ignore   d. match

_____ 2. **extract**   a. insert   b. withdraw   c. advise   d. pull

_____ 3. **adjacent**   a. round   b. touching   c. distant   d. angular

_____ 4. **perimeter**   a. border   b. center   c. angle   d. square

_____ 5. **portable**   a. movable   b. fixed   c. lightweight   d. missing

_____ 6. **refer**   a. mention   b. wonder   c. expect   d. overlook

_____ 7. **permission**   a. refusal   b. request   c. approval   d. demand

_____ 8. **submit**   a. raise   b. deliver   c. evaluate   d. withdraw

D. Match Ideas

On the line before each item, write the target word from the list below that is most clearly related to the situation described in the sentence. Use each word only once.

      percent   rate   ratio   subscription

_____ **1.** The nurse counts the number of heartbeats per minute.

_____ **2.** Part of a hundred.

_____ **3.** Lori has signed up and paid to receive a monthly tennis magazine.

_____ **4.** The middle school has one teacher for every twenty students.

E. Identify Roots in Related Words

Underline the root shared by each pair of words. Then define the words on the lines provided.

1. portable: _____

    transport: _____

2. conform: _____

    reformer: _____

3. contract: _____

    extract: _____

4. submit: _____

    transmit: _____

5. extend: _____

    extension: _____

6. scribble: _____

    prescribe: _____

UNIT 3

F. Analyze Context and Meaning

Each of the following statements contains at least one boldfaced target word. On the line before the statement, write *T* if it is true. Write *F* if it is false.

_____ **1.** The time between the acts of a play is called the **transportation.**

_____ **2.** The **decimal** .09 is the same as the **fraction** 9/10.

_____ **3.** The number 4 is a **factor** of 8.

_____ **4.** An **integer** may be a **positive** or **negative** number but cannot be zero..

_____ **5.** A plus sign has **parallel** lines and **perpendicular** lines.

_____ **6.** If you want to know how much paint to buy for the ceiling in your room, you have to measure its **area.**

G. Use Words in Context

On the line before each sentence, write the target word that best completes the sentence. Use each target word only once. Not all choices will be used.

circumference	complementary	cylinder	denominator
diameter	isosceles	perimeter	polygon
proportion	volume		

_____ **1.** The bottom number of a fraction is called a _____.

_____ **2.** The size of the space inside a cube is called its _____.

_____ **3.** An _____ triangle has two equal sides.

_____ **4.** A can of vegetables is usually shaped like a _____.

_____ **5.** Angles that together add up to 90 degrees are said to be

_____.

_____ **6.** The distance across a circle through its center is its _____.

_____ **7.** The equation 2/3 = 8/12 is an example of a _____.

_____ **8.** The five-sided Pentagon building in Washington, D.C., is a

_____.

Feature: Similes and Metaphors

WHAT IS IT?

Figurative language Figurative language is language that uses words in an imaginative way to express ideas that are not literally true. For example, if Julie says, "I cried a river," she is not talking about a real river. Instead, she is using words figuratively to describe how much she cried.

Two common types of figurative language are similes and metaphors. Both are forms of comparison. A **simile** compares two unlike things by using words such as *like*, *as*, *than*, or *resembles*. A **metaphor** compares two unlike things by stating that one actually is the other.

Figurative Language	Things Compared	Meaning
Simile: His hair is like silk.	hair / silk	His hair is smooth and shiny.
Metaphor: Life is a jigsaw puzzle.	life / jigsaw puzzle	Life has many confusing pieces.

WHY IT MATTERS

When you understand figurative language, you can appreciate the creative ways in which writers express their ideas and emotions. When you learn how to use figurative language, your own writing will come alive with vivid images and comparisons.

EXERCISE 1: Identify Similes and Metaphors

On the line before each sentence, write *S* if it contains a simile. Write *M* if it contains a metaphor. Underline the two things being compared. Then circle the letter of the choice that best explains what the figurative language means.

_____ 1. The library was as quiet as the bottom of the sea.
    a. The library was very quiet.
    b. The library was very noisy.

_____ 2. The grass is a green velvet carpet.
    a. The grass feels soft and thick.
    b. The grass covers a hard surface.

_____ 3. Jo stared at the test paper as if it were an enemy.
    a. Jo viewed the test with fear and anger.
    b. Jo saw the test as a living thing.

_____ 4. When Grandfather gets angry, he is a fire-breathing dragon.
    a. When Grandfather gets angry, smoke comes out of his nostrils.
    b. When Grandfather gets angry, he can frighten others.

_____ 5. Good reporters are like cameras.
    a. Good reporters are high-priced and flashy.
    b. Good reporters accurately record what they see.

EXERCISE 2: Understand Similes and Metaphors

For each sentence, indicate whether the boldfaced words are a simile or a metaphor by underlining the correct choice in parentheses. Then explain the meaning of each comparison.

EXAMPLE   That excuse is **as flimsy as tissue**. (<u>simile</u>/metaphor)
meaning: *That excuse is very weak*

1. The leafless tree **looked like a skeleton**. (_____/metaphor)

   meaning: _____

2. Marianne is **a library of sports facts and figures**. (simile/_____)

   meaning: _____

3. The storm cloud was **like a black curtain**. (_____/metaphor)

   meaning: _____

4. Evan's home is hectic, but his room is **an island in a stormy sea**. (simile/_____)

   meaning: _____

EXERCISE 3: Make Words Your Own

Complete each sentence by writing a simile or a metaphor, as indicated. On the line after the sentence, write the meaning of your figurative language.

1. Metaphor: The sunshine was _____

   meaning: _____

   _____

2. Simile: The small, dark room was _____

   meaning: _____

   _____

3. Metaphor: A good friend is _____

   meaning: _____

   _____

4. Simile: Losing the championship game hurt_____

   meaning: _____

   _____

LESSON 13 Greek Roots and Related Words I

Target Words	Root/Combining Form	Meaning
biographer, *n.*	*bio*	life
biography, *n*	*graph*	to write, draw, or record
graphic, *adj.*		
geographer, *n.*	*geo*	earth
geographical, *adj.*		
geological, *adj.*	*logy*	the science or study of
geologist, *n.*		
geology, *n.*		
phonograph, *n.*	*phon*	sound
symphony, *n.*		
photographer, *n.*	*photo*	light
photography, *n.*		

GETTING STARTED

Remember that **roots** are words parts that cannot stand alone. Like Latin, Greek has
contributed many roots to English. Greek roots are also known as **combining forms**.
Throughout time, inventors and scientists have used Greek roots to name many new
concepts and devices, from *photography* to *phonograph*. In this lesson you will study
words containing the Greek roots *bio*, *graph*, *geo*, *logy*, *phon*, and *photo*. Many of
these words combine *graph* with other roots. What do the words in the cluster below
have to do with writing, drawing, or recording?

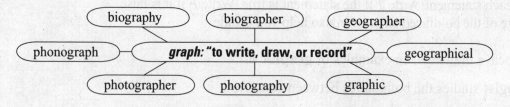

I. Practice the Words

EXERCISE 1: Understand Greek Roots

Put separate boxes around the two roots in each target word. Then briefly explain how the
meaning of the word reflects the meaning of its roots.

1. geology: _____

2. photography: _____

EXERCISE 2: Identify Roots and Meanings

Underline the root or roots in each target word on the left. Then match each word with its correct meaning on the right. Write the letter of the correct meaning in the space provided. Use each meaning only once.

1. biographer _____

a. the study of the rocks, history, and inner structure of Earth

2. biography _____

b. relating to the study of Earth's features, nations, and people

3. geographer _____

c. a machine that plays back sounds by means of a needle coming in contact with a rotating disk

4. geographical _____

d. the process of recording images on light-sensitive surfaces

5. geological _____

e. someone who studies the rocks, history, and inner structure of Earth

6. geologist _____

f. someone who records images on light-sensitive surfaces

7. geology _____

g. an account of a person's life written by another

8. graphic _____

h. someone who studies Earth's features, nations, and people

9. phonograph _____

i. relating to the study of Earth's rocks, history, and inner structure

10. photographer _____

j. a long piece of music for a full orchestra, usually divided into four movements

11. photography _____

k. someone who writes or tells another person's life story

12. symphony _____

l. relating to written or pictorial representation; detailed, vivid, and lifelike

EXERCISE 3: Determine True/False

On the line before each statement, write *T* if the statement is true. Write *F* if it is false. Use your knowledge of the boldfaced target words to help you decide.

_____ **1.** Ancient cave drawings are examples of **graphic** art.

_____ **2.** A **geologist** studies the boundaries between countries.

_____ **3.** Light is important to a **photographer.**

_____ **4.** A **symphony** is a machine that plays music.

_____ **5.** A **geographer** may study an earthquake.

_____ **6.** A **biography** is a work of fiction.

EXERCISE 4: Use Words in Context

Using your knowledge of paragraph clues, select the target word from the list that best completes each sentence and write it on the line provided. Use each word only once.

biographer	biography	geographical	geological
geologist	photographer	photography	

1. Ansel Adams is a _____ who is known for his black-and-white images of the American wilderness. His method of _____ uses light and shadow to create a range of tones, from white to black.

2. One of Ansel Adams's most famous photos is of the _____ formation known as Half Dome. It is an enormous granite crest that rises more than 4,700 feet above the floor of the _____ area known as the Yosemite Valley. A _____ who has studied the history of Earth can confirm that Half Dome was formed about 93 million years ago.

EXERCISE 5: Analyze Context and Meaning

Use your knowledge of the target words to help you answer each question. Write the letter of the answer on the line before the question.

_____ 1. Who writes a book about another person?   **a.** biographer   **b.** photographer

_____ 2. Who helps create maps of nations?   **a.** geographer   **b.** geologist

_____ 3. Which subject is part of earth science?   **a.** photography   **b.** geology

_____ 4. What kind of survey shows layers of the earth? **a.** geological   **b.** geographical

EXERCISE 6: Use Target Words in Writing

On a separate sheet of paper, write a one-paragraph description of the natural features, the climate, and the people in the area where you live. Use at least two target words in your description.

II. Vocabulary Challenge

EXERCISE 7: Extend Your Vocabulary

Fill in this word cluster with six words that contain the root *phon*. Do not use any words from the target list. Write the definition of each word on the lines provided. Your definitions should reflect the meaning of the root *phon*. Check your answers in a dictionary.

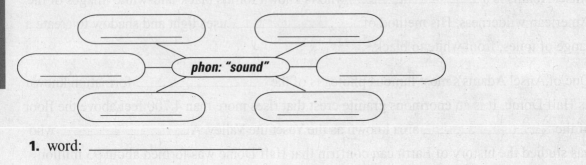

1. word: _____

   meaning: _____

2. word: _____

   meaning: _____

3. word: _____

   meaning: _____

4. word: _____

   meaning: _____

5. word: _____

   meaning: _____

   _____

6. word: _____

   meaning: _____

Wordsmart: Etymology

Geology is just one example of the many branches of science, medicine, and other fields named by combining *logy* with another Greek root. *Biology*, for instance, is the science that studies living things; *cardiology* is the branch of medicine that deals with the heart (*cardi* is the Greek root for "heart"). What other words with *logy* do you know? In each word, what do you think might be the meaning of the Greek root that combines with *logy*?

LESSON 14 Words Used in Science

Target Words
biome, *n.* a large geographical area with distinctive plant and animal groups that are adapted to the climate and conditions of that environment
ecology, *n.* the science that deals with how living things relate to their environment
ecosystem, *n.* a community in nature, with the living things that inhabit it reacting to one another and to the physical environment
experiment, *n., v.* a test done to prove how or why something happens; to conduct such a test
hypothesis, *n.* an idea of how something happens that can be tested by experiment
organism, *n.* a living thing
photosynthesis, *n.* the process by which green plants use sunlight to manufacture their food
resource, *n.* the available supply of a natural material
result, *n., v.* the consequence or effect; to occur as a consequence
species, *n.* a group of living things that can breed with one another
topography, *n.* the surface features of a region such as mountains and rivers; the study and mapping of such features
variable, *n., adj.* something that can change in value, quality, or quantity; subject to change; not constant

GETTING STARTED

Science has a special vocabulary that includes technical words and everyday words that are used in special ways. Learning the vocabulary of science can help you better understand the science you learn in school. It can also improve your writing and speaking skills by giving you more words to describe your environment.

I. Practice the Words

EXERCISE 1: Break It Down

Some of the target words in this lesson contain Greek roots that you learned in lesson 13. Underline the roots in the target words in the left column and match each word with a root meaning in the right column. Write the letter of the correct meaning in the space next to each word. Use each root meaning only once.

Target Word

1. biome _____

2. ecology _____

3. photosynthesis _____

4. topography _____

Root Meaning

a. to write, draw, or record

b. light

c. life

d. the science or study of

EXERCISE 2: Match Words to Context

Using your knowledge of sentence clues, circle the letter of the target word that best completes each sentence.

1. A natural supply of water is an important _____ for a community to have.
   a. organism   **b.** resource   **c.** species   **d.** biome

2. To make food by the process known as _____, plants must have sunlight.
   a. photosynthesis   **b.** hypothesis   **c.** topography   **d.** ecology

3. A desert is a _____ with very little rainfall.
   a. biome   **b.** resource   **c.** species   **d.** variable

4. In the science of _____, we learn about the relationship of living things and their environment.
   a. photosynthesis   **b.** hypothesis   **c.** topography   **d.** ecology

5. A pond is an _____ in which many different plants and animals function as one unit.
   a. organism   **b.** experiment   **c.** ecosystem   **d.** ecology

6. Every _____ that lives in the pond, from bacteria to fish to frogs, has a role to play.
   a. organism   **b.** experiment   **c.** variable   **d.** biome

7. People are all part of the human _____, no matter where they come from.
   a. ecosystem   **b.** species   **c.** variable   **d.** biome

8. The map showed the _____ of the region, with raised areas signifying mountains.
   a. photosynthesis   **b.** hypothesis   **c.** ecosystem   **d.** topography

9. If you want to prove or disprove a _____, you have to test it.
   a. photosynthesis   **b.** hypothesis   **c.** organism   **d.** species

10. The amount of liquid in the test tube was constant, but the temperature was _____.
    a. hypothesis   **b.** species   **c.** variable   **d.** result

11. An _____ in a laboratory is easier to control than a test you perform at home.
    a. result   **b.** resource   **c.** topography   **d.** experiment

12. Samuel's beautiful piano playing was the _____ of much practice.
    a. result   **b.** organism   **c.** topography   **d.** ecosystem

EXERCISE 3: Solve a Paragraph Puzzle

For each choice in parentheses, circle the target word that makes the most sense.

Knowing the science of (ecology, topography) will make you aware of the many (species, variables) that make up Earth's different living communities. It will help you understand the delicate balance between each (organism, resource), or living thing, and the (ecosystem, ecology) it inhabits. Consider the relationship between plants and animals. In (photosynthesis, hypothesis), the process plants use to make their food, the plants take in carbon dioxide from the air and emit oxygen. Animals, in turn, breathe in that oxygen and breathe out carbon dioxide. In addition, animals use plants for food. Therefore, if harm comes to the plants in a particular (biome, topography), the (result, experiment) would harm animals, too.

EXERCISE 4: Analyze Word Relationships

Each question below contains one boldfaced target word. On the lines provided, answer the question with a statement that accurately uses the target word in parentheses.

EXAMPLE   What factor changes each time you conduct this **experiment?**
          (variable)   *The amount of sunlight is a variable in the experiment.*

1. Why might a scientist conduct an **experiment**?

   (hypothesis) _____

2. What do plants produce in the process of **photosynthesis**?

   (result) _____

3. Name one animal **species** that lives in a hot climate.

   (organism) _____

4. In studying **ecology,** what can you learn about the characteristics of a desert?

   (biome) _____

5. What natural **resource** is essential to all living things?

   (ecosystem) _____

6. What kinds of animals are suited to an area with a mountainous **topography?**

   (species) _____

UNIT 4

EXERCISE 5: Use Target Words in Writing

On a separate sheet of paper, write a sentence on a science topic for each of the target words listed at the beginning of this lesson. Be sure your sentences show that you understand what the words mean.

EXAMPLE   biome: *A rainforest is a type of biome in which plants thrive.*

EXERCISE 6: Speaking

Discuss one of the following topics with a small group of your classmates.

1. Describe a science experiment you or your teacher conducted, or one that you read about in your science textbook. Use at least three target words in your discussion.

2. Discuss an ecosystem in your area. Use at least three target words in your discussion.

II. Vocabulary Challenge

EXERCISE 7: Recognize Parts of Speech

Some of the target words in this lesson can be used as more than one part of speech. On the blank line before each sentence write *N* if the boldfaced target word is a noun, *V* if it is a verb, or *A* if it is an adjective. Use a dictionary if necessary, or refer to the definitions at the beginning of the lesson.

1. _____ Her **experiment** proved that plants need sunlight in order to grow.

2. _____ The cook wanted to **experiment** with a new dessert recipe.

3. _____ In the springtime the weather is often **variable.**

4. _____ Quality is sometimes a more important **variable** than cost.

5. _____ The **result** of his outburst was a week's detention.

6. _____ Overeating can **result** in obesity.

Wordsmart: Etymology

Eco, which appears in *ecology* and *ecosystem*, comes from the Greek word *oikos*, meaning "house." *Ecology* is the science that studies the "house," or environment, in which living things reside, and an *ecosystem* is a community of organisms that live in a particular place and function as a single unit. The same Greek root appears in the word *economy*, which literally means "the management of a household" but also refers to financial management in general.

LESSON
15 Greek Roots and Related Words II

Target Words	Root/ Combining Form	Meaning
asteroid, n.	aster/astro	star
astronaut, n.		
astronomer, n.		
chronicle, n., v.	chron	time
chronological, adj.		
chronology, n.		
disaster, n.		
mechanical, adj.	mechan	machine, tool
mechanize, v.		
technical, adj.	techn	art, skill
technician, n.		
technology, n.		

GETTING STARTED

Technology may be modern, but the word *technology* has ancient roots—it goes back to the Greek word for "art" or "skill." In this lesson, you will study several Greek roots, also called **combining forms**—*aster/astro, chron, mechan,* and *techn.* Recall that **roots** are word parts that cannot stand alone. Roots must be combined with other word parts to form words. A group of words that share the same root is called a **word family**. For example, the target words include *technical, technician,* and *technology,* which are all related words that contain the root *techn.*

Sometimes it is hard to see the relationship between a root's original meaning and what a word means in modern English. For example, a *disaster* is "a terrible or harmful event." The word combines the negative prefix *dis-* with the root *aster,* which means "star." The meaning of the word is based in the ancient belief that the position of the stars played a role in controlling human affairs. It was believed that a terrible or harmful event was caused by a bad or unlucky star—a "dis-aster."

I. Practice the Words

EXERCISE 1: Understand Greek Roots

Circle the Greek root in each target word below. Then explain how the meaning of the word relates to the Greek root it contains.

1. astronaut   _____

2. chronology   _____

3. mechanize   _____

4. technical   _____

EXERCISE 2: Identify Roots and Meanings

Underline the root in each target word on the left. Then match each word with its correct meaning on the right. Write the letter of the correct meaning in the space provided. Use a dictionary if necessary. The first one has been done for you.

1. asteroid _____   **a.** a record of historical events; to tell or write the history of

2. astronaut _____   **b.** relating to machines or tools

3. astronomer _____   **c.** having or requiring special skill or knowledge, especially in a mechanical or scientific field

4. chronicle _____   **d.** the application of science to industrial or commercial purposes

5. chronological _____   **e.** a scientist who studies the stars, planets, and outer space

6. chronology _____   **f.** to equip with machinery

7. disaster _____   **g.** an ill-starred, or harmful, event

8. mechanical _____   **h.** a specialist in the technical details of a subject

9. mechanize _____   **i.** in time order, or the order of occurrence

10. technical _____   **j.** a small, planet-like body that revolves around the sun, usually between the orbits of Mars and Jupiter

11. technician _____   **k.** a list or arrangement in time order, or order of occurrence

12. technology _____   **l.** someone trained to make flights in outer space

EXERCISE 3: Apply Meaning to Context

Circle the letter of the best answer to each question. Use your knowledge of the boldfaced target words to help you decide.

1. Which of these is arranged **chronologically?**
   a. a phone book   **b.** a timeline   **c.** a table of contents   **d.** an index

2. Where would you find an **astronaut** on a mission?
   a. at sea   **b.** in space   **c.** on land   **d.** underground

3. What would you expect in a **technical** report?
   a. strong opinions   **b.** poetry   **c.** mechanical details   **d.** lots of humor

4. Where might you see an **asteroid?**
   a. underground   **b.** in a treetop   **c.** near a pond   **d.** in the night sky

5. Which of these is a product of modern **technology?**
   a. freckles   **b.** mountains   **c.** computers   **d.** sleepiness

6. What would the **chronicle** of a people provide?
   a. their history   **b.** their songs   **c.** their recipes   **d.** their finances

EXERCISE 4: Determine True/False

On the line before each statement, write *T* if the statement is true. Write *F* if it is false. Use your knowledge of the boldfaced target words to help you decide.

_____ **1.** Most people welcome a great **disaster.**

_____ **2.** A **chronology** lists events in order of importance.

_____ **3.** To **mechanize** a mailroom, a firm might install stamping and sorting machines.

_____ **4.** An **astronomer** studies the human body and the diseases that can harm it.

_____ **5.** A lab **technician** must be skilled in using lab equipment.

_____ **6.** A **mechanical** toy is one that runs like a little machine.

EXERCISE 5: Use Words in Context

Using your knowledge of sentence clues, select a target word from the list to complete each sentence and write it on the line provided. Use each word only once.

astronaut	astronomer	chronicle	chronology
disaster	mechanize	technical	technology

1. A tornado is a natural _____ that can level an entire town with its violent winds.

2. From electric alarm clocks to washing machines, _____ has produced many common household conveniences.

3. Bede was a medieval scholar who used both written and oral sources to

_____ the history of England.

4. The _____ trained in a zero-gravity environment before going into space.

5. During the Industrial Revolution, many textile mills installed power-driven equipment to

_____ the process of producing cloth.

6. The students created a _____ of major events that occurred during each year of World War II.

7. The instructions for using the new digital camera had many _____ details that were hard to follow.

8. The _____ used a high-powered telescope to study the moons of the planet Saturn.

EXERCISE 6: Use Target Words in Writing

On a separate sheet of paper, write a paragraph about a discovery or an invention that has improved your life. Use at least three target words in your paragraph.

II. Vocabulary Challenge

EXERCISE 7: Extend Your Vocabulary

Use what you have learned about the Greek roots *astro/aster, chron, mechan,* and *techn* to answer these questions about more words that contain those roots. Write the letter of the best answer on the line before each question.

_____ 1. What does the flower called an **aster** look like?

     a. It is round in shape.   **c.** It has petals of two different colors.

     b. It is star shaped.   **d.** It is long and thin.

_____ 2. How often does a **chronic** problem occur?

     a. never   **c.** regularly

     b. rarely   **d.** as needed

_____ 3. What does perfecting your **technique** mean?

     a. improving your skill   **c.** being a role model

     b. being a kind person   **d.** answering test questions correctly

_____ 4. What must swimmers do to be **synchronized**?

     a. wear bathing caps   **c.** make the same moves at the same time

     b. swim with great speed   **d.** compete with each other

_____ 5. What is an **astrologer**?

     a. someone who studies stars   **c.** someone who works with his or her hands

     b. someone who studies time   **d.** someone who manages factory workers

_____ 6. What might a **mechanic** do with a truck**?**

     a. paint a new logo on it   **c.** pay its parking tickets

     b. buy it   **d.** repair it

Wordsmart: Etymology

Astronaut combines the Greek root *astro* with the Greek root *naut,* meaning "sailor." An *astronaut* is literally "a sailor of the stars." *Cosmonaut,* the Russian equivalent of *astronaut,* combines the root *astro* with the Greek root *cosmo,* meaning "world" or "universe." A *cosmonaut* is a "sailor of the universe."

LESSON 16 Words Related to Time

Target Words
ancestry, *n.* the people from whom someone descends
centennial, *n., adj.* a hundred-year anniversary; relating to such an anniversary
colonial, *adj.* referring to a time when the thirteen original colonies that formed the United States were still possessions of Britain
decade, *n.* a period of ten years; a group or series of ten
eternity, *n.* time without beginning or end; time that lasts forever
generation, *n.* the average period between the birth of parents and the birth of their offspring; all the people born at about the same time
interval, *n.* the time between two events or time periods
midday, *n.* the middle of the day; noon
millennium, *n.* a period of a thousand years; a thousand-year anniversary
overnight, *adj., adv.* lasting for or staying the night; during or through the night
primitive, *adj.* dating from or relating to very early times
sundial, *n.* an instrument that shows time by the position of a shadow cast by a pointer on a dial marked in hours

GETTING STARTED

Morning, evening, week, month, past, present—humans have all sorts of words for time periods and relationships involving time. In this lesson you will study words that describe different aspects of time. Learning these words will help you understand historical concepts and be more precise in your own writing.

I. Practice the Words

EXERCISE 1: Solve a Paragraph Puzzle

Using the target words and your knowledge of context clues such as definition and contrast, fill in all the blank spaces in this paragraph. Use each word only once. Be sure the words fit grammatically into the sentences.

In 2001, as the world entered a new _____, our town celebrated its _____, or

hundredth birthday. The people who settled here in 1901 were a _____ of rugged

pioneers who traced their family history, or _____, back to the people who settled

in _____ Virginia at the time of the Revolutionary War. Life in the West in that first

_____ of the 20th century was _____ by today's modern standards. Some people

used the shadow on a _____ to tell time, but others relied on the _____ train that

arrived at lunchtime. Even _____ mail did not always arrive the next day. The _____

between when a letter was sent from the East and when it arrived in the West could be a week

or more. To modern Americans, that length of time seems like an _____ .

UNIT 4

EXERCISE 2: Match Ideas to Context

Select a target word from the list to complete each sentence and write it on the line provided. Use each word only once.

ancestry	centennial	colonial	decade	eternity	generation
interval	midday	millennium	overnight	primitive	sundial

1. The sun is at its highest point in the sky and the clock chimes twelve times

   at _____ .

2. _____ express mail is scheduled to arrive the next day.

3. In _____ times, people used simple stone tools and lived in caves.

4. Children are a person's descendants, but one's _____ includes one's parents and grandparents.

5. People long ago used the shadows on a _____ to tell time.

6. During the _____ period in the 17ᵗʰ century, the British possessions in North America had not yet won their independence.

7. A ring is a symbol of love that lasts through _____ because a ring has no beginning or end.

8. California became a state in 1850 and celebrated its _____ in 1950.

9. When the boy next door completed his first _____ of life, his birthday cake was decorated with ten candles.

10. When Alice and Ryan marry and raise a family, their children will be the

    next _____ .

11. There was a three-day _____ between the two playoff games.

12. The vase was 2,000 years old, dating back to the first _____ A.D.

EXERCISE 3: Match Words and Numbers

On the line before each item on the left, write the letter of the target word on the right that correctly defines the numerical expression.

_____ **1.** 1888–1988   **a.** millennium

_____ **2.** 1001–2000   **b.** centennial

_____ **3.** 11 P.M.–8 A.M.   **c.** overnight

_____ **4.** 12:00 P.M.   **d.** midday

EXERCISE 4: Determine True/False

On the line before each statement, write *T* if the statement is true. Write *F* if it is false. Use your knowledge of the boldfaced target words to help you decide.

_____ **1.** Nobody tries to sleep on an **overnight** plane flight.

_____ **2.** The American Revolution ended the **colonial** period of American history.

_____ **3.** During the **interval** between TV shows, some people go to the kitchen for a snack.

_____ **4.** A **generation** lasts around thirty years.

_____ **5.** Most people can trace their **ancestry** to **primitive** times.

_____ **6.** An **eternity** is shorter than a **millennium**.

_____ **7.** A school celebrates its **centennial** three **decades** after it was established.

_____ **8.** At **midday**, a **sundial** will indicate that it is 12 o'clock.

EXERCISE 5: Identify Synonyms and Antonyms

On the line before each pair of words, write *S* if the words are synonyms. Write *A* if they are antonyms. The target word in each pair is boldfaced.

_____ **1. midday**/noon   _____ **4. ancestry**/descendants

_____ **2. primitive**/modern   _____ **5. eternity**/infinity

_____ **3. interval**/period   _____ **6. colonial**/recent

EXERCISE 6: Use Target Words in Writing

On a separate sheet of paper, write a sentence about time for each of the target words listed at the beginning of this lesson. Be sure your sentences show that you understand what the words mean.

EXAMPLE   interval   *In the interval between classes, Terry does stretching exercises.*

EXERCISE 7: Speaking

Discuss your favorite time period in history with a small group of your classmates. Use at least three target words in your discussion.

UNIT 4

II. Vocabulary Challenge

EXERCISE 8: Word Play

Use the clues to fill in this crossword puzzle with the target words.

ACROSS

4. From 7 P.M. to 7 A.M.

5. 1,000 years

8. Siblings and cousins of the same age in a family

9. 1930–1939

12. Those who came before

DOWN

1. A solar clock

2. What the U.S. celebrated in 1876

3. From the Stone Age

6. Noontime

7. The period in between

10. Ocurring before the American Revolution

11. It takes forever

Wordsmart: Etymology

Primitive contains the Latin root *prim*, which means "first." Something *primitive* goes back to the first times or is in its original style. The root appears in many other English words, such as *primary*, "first in time or importance," and *prime,* which shares the idea of "first in importance." The flower called a *primrose* blooms in early spring, the "first rose." A *primer* (pronounced with the short *i* of *primitive*) is a school book for beginning students. A *primer* (pronounced with the long *i* of *prime*) is a first or base coat of paint. *Primates* (pronounced with long *i*) are the order of animals (including human beings) considered first in intelligence in the animal world.

Check Your Knowledge: Unit 4

By now you have added 48 new words to your vocabulary. Test your ability to use these words in the following exercises.

A. Determine Meaning from Context

On the line before each sentence, write the letter of the word or phrase that is closest in meaning to the boldfaced target word. Use the context clues to help you decide.

____ **1.** A virus may not be an **organism**, since some scientists feel it is not alive.
  a. living thing   **b.** belief   **c.** useful product   **d.** musical instrument

____ **2.** An explosion could **result** from mixing flammable chemicals.
  a. be dangerous   **b.** be a cause of   **c.** be a consequence   **d.** be false

____ **3.** Her **graphic** description of the city made me feel as if I were there.
  a. pleasant   **b.** oral   **c.** brief and unclear   **d.** vivid and detailed

____ **4.** She did the task in a **mechanical** way, with no emotion or enthusiasm.
  a. unscientific   **b.** confused   **c.** machinelike   **d.** humanlike

____ **5.** The **chronology** of Marie Curie's life listed her achievements by date.
  a. document   **b.** timeline   **c.** science article   **d.** life story

____ **6.** Is the outcome **variable**, or is it always the same?
  a. changeable   **b.** similar   **c.** clear and precise   **d.** useful to know

____ **7.** Paul Revere lived in **colonial** times, before America won independence.
  a. dangerous   **b.** modern   **c.** before Columbus   **d.** before the Revolution

____ **8.** Luis's father uses an old **phonograph** to play his music.
  a. record player   **b.** camera   **c.** set of instructions   **d.** compact disk

____ **9.** The **biography** traced Abraham Lincoln's experiences from childhood on.
  a. news feature   **b.** life story   **c.** presentation   **d.** oil painting

____ **10.** When you are in a hurry, even a few minutes can seem like an **eternity**.
  a. a good time   **b.** a short time   **c.** an endless time   **d.** the distant past

B. Identify Synonyms

On the line before each item, write the letter of the word that is closest in meaning to the boldfaced target word.

_____ **1. experiment**	**a.** science	**b.** test	**c.** experience	**d.** change
_____ **2. hypothesis**	**a.** certainty	**b.** answer	**c.** report	**d.** theory
_____ **3. chronicle**	**a.** pamphlet	**b.** history	**c.** delivery	**d.** textbook
_____ **4. mechanical**	**a.** automatic	**b.** bold	**c.** helpful	**d.** natural
_____ **5. resource**	**a.** outcome	**b.** version	**c.** supply	**d.** shortage
_____ **6. eternity**	**a.** infinity	**b.** time	**c.** measurement	**d.** exterior
_____ **7. technical**	**a.** negative	**b.** careful	**c.** unimportant	**d.** detailed
_____ **8. interval**	**a.** weakness	**b.** discussion	**c.** period	**d.** value

C. Identify Antonyms

On the line before each item, write the letter of the word that is most nearly the opposite of the boldfaced target word.

_____ **1. disaster**	**a.** occurrence	**b.** confusion	**c.** blessing	**d.** horror
_____ **2. colonial**	**a.** modern	**b.** patriotic	**c.** old-fashioned	**d.** curly
_____ **3. ancestry**	**a.** sponsors	**b.** offspring	**c.** forefathers	**d.** humans
_____ **4. result**	**a.** problem	**b.** outcome	**c.** question	**d.** contrast
_____ **5. variable**	**a.** different	**b.** successful	**c.** imaginative	**d.** constant
_____ **6. graphic**	**a.** vivid	**b.** wonderful	**c.** vague	**d.** gloomy
_____ **7. primitive**	**a.** crude	**b.** first	**c.** sophisticated	**d.** wild
_____ **8. midday**	**a.** yesterday	**b.** tomorrow	**c.** noon	**d.** midnight

D. Match Ideas

On the line before each job description in the left column, write the letter of the matching job in the right column. Use each word only once.

_____ **1.** a writer who tells another person's life story

_____ **2.** someone trained to make flights in outer space

_____ **3.** someone who records images on light-sensitive surfaces

_____ **4.** a scientist who studies the stars, the planets, and outer space

_____ **5.** a scientist who studies the rocks, history, and inner structure of the earth

_____ **6.** someone skilled in any applied, or practical, science

_____ **7.** someone who studies the earth's surface and the nations and cultures on it

a. astronaut

b. astronomer

c. biographer

d. geographer

e. geologist

f. photographer

g. technician

E. Determine True/False

Each of the following statements contains at least one boldfaced target word. On the line before the statement, write *T* if the statement is true. Write *F* if it is false.

_____ **1. Photosynthesis** is the process by which **photographers** develop film.

_____ **2.** The following **decades** are in **chronological** order: 1950s, 1960s, 1970s.

_____ **3.** A **sundial** can tell you when it is **midday.**

_____ **4.** A desert is a **biome** with very little rainfall.

_____ **5.** A typical **ecosystem** includes plants but not animals.

_____ **6.** Animals from different **species** often breed together.

_____ **7.** If it exists for a **millennium,** a city could celebrate ten **centennials** in that time.

F. Use Words in Context

Choose the target word below that best completes each sentence, and write it on the line provided. Use each target word only once. Not all target words will be used.

ancestry	decade	experiment	generation
interval	mechanize	overnight	symphony

1. In the 1800s, newly invented machines helped _____ farms.

2. Older people worry about the younger _____ .

3. A scientist needs to _____ to see if his or her ideas are true.

4. Do this homework _____ so that it is ready by tomorrow.

5. In one _____, from 1990 to 2000, Internet use became widespread.

G. Identify Roots in Related Words

Underline the Greek root shared by each group of words. Write the meaning of each word on the lines provided.

1. biography: _____

_____

photography: _____

_____

topography: _____

_____

2. geographical: _____

_____

geological: _____

_____

3. ecology: _____

_____

geology: _____

_____

technology: _____

_____

4. phonograph: _____

_____

symphony: _____

_____

5. asteroid: _____

_____

disaster: _____

_____

LESSON 18 Words About Ancient Civilizations

Target Words

antique, *n.* an object that has special value because of its age

caste, *n.* a hereditary social class in Hindu society

chariot, *n.* an ancient, two-wheeled vehicle drawn by horses

conquest, *n.* the act of defeating and controlling by force

empire, *n.* a group of countries or territories ruled by a single authority

invade, *n.* to enter by force in order to conquer

pageant, *n.* a spectacular procession, parade, or celebration; during the Middle Ages, a festival in which religious plays were performed

pharaoh, *n.* a king of ancient Egypt

pyramid, *n.* a huge structure with a square base and four triangular sides, used in ancient Egypt as a royal tomb

reign, *n., v.* the exercise of supreme authority, as by a king, queen, or other monarch; the period during which a monarch rules; to rule as a supreme power

sacred, *adj.* dedicated to or set apart for religious reasons; holy

tyrant, *n.* a ruler who governs with unlimited power; a harsh or cruel ruler

GETTING STARTED

The lives of people who lived long ago were different from our lives today. Ancient Egyptians were ruled by a pharaoh and were buried in tombs called pyramids. Ancient Romans rode in vehicles called chariots and were part of a large empire. In this lesson you will study words that are associated with ancient civilizations. Learning these words will help in your study of ancient cultures.

I. Practice the Words

EXERCISE 1: Solve a Paragraph Puzzle

Use ten target words and your knowledge of context clues such as restatement to fill in the blank spaces in this paragraph. Use each word only once, and be sure the words fit grammatically into the sentences.

At the museum, we learned about a _____, or king, who ruled ancient

Egypt. He was a harsh _____ who did not allow anyone to question his

authority. He was also an ambitious military leader who was able to _____

neighboring lands. Each forceful _____ increased the size of the

Egyptian _____. When his _____, or the time during

which he ruled, was over, he was buried in a _____ with objects that were

_____ in the religion of ancient Egypt. Some of these objects are on display

at the museum. The most valuable _____ in the collection is a painted

vehicle that looks like a Roman _____.

EXERCISE 2: Match Ideas to Context

Select a target word from the list to complete each sentence. Use each word only once.

antique	caste	chariot	conquest	empire	invade
pharaoh	pageant	pyramid	reign	sacred	tyrant

1. Romans in the first century C.E. feared the emperor Caligula because he was

a cruel _____ .

2. In the _____ of the Aztecs by Spain, the Aztecs were defeated and overrun.

3. The Ganges River in India is a _____ site. In Hindu mythology, it was once a river of heaven that flowed across the sky.

4. The Egyptian _____ Tutankhamen, known as King Tut, was buried in the Valley of the Kings.

5. _____ racing was a popular sport in ancient Rome that was dangerous to both the drivers and the horses.

6. Mardi Gras is a colorful _____ that includes music, dancing, costumes, parties, and parades.

7. At one time, Hindus of one _____ could not mix with those of another.

8. The _____ of the emperor Julius Caesar lasted from 49 B.C. until his assassination in 44 B.C.

9. A coin from ancient Greece would be a valuable _____ .

10. Genghis Khan wanted to _____ China to acquire its great wealth.

11. Through a series of conquests, Alexander the Great extended the Macedonian

_____ all the way to India.

12. The _____ at Giza is made of more than 2 million stone blocks, each weighing at least 2 1/2 tons.

EXERCISE 3: Use Target Words in Writing

On a separate sheet of paper, write a sentence about ancient civilizations for each of the target words listed at the beginning of this lesson. Be sure your sentences show that you understand what the words mean.

EXAMPLE empire *Rome became a great empire by extending its rule to many lands.*

EXERCISE 4: Identify Synonyms

On the line before each item, write the letter of the word that is closest in meaning to the boldfaced target word.

_____ **1. antique**   **a.** object   **b.** possession   **c.** relic   **d.** vehicle

_____ **2. conquest**   **a.** damage   **b.** escape   **c.** search   **d.** victory

_____ **3. empire**   **a.** palace   **b.** kingdom   **c.** belief   **d.** triumph

_____ **4. invade**   **a.** overrun   **b.** deliver   **c.** benefit   **d.** escape

_____ **5. pageant**   **a.** display   **b.** garden   **c.** book   **d.** document

_____ **6. reign**   **a.** strap   **b.** demand   **c.** carriage   **d.** rule

_____ **7. sacred**   **a.** dark   **b.** holy   **c.** mysterious   **d.** ancient

_____ **8. tyrant**   **a.** citizen   **b.** scientist   **c.** mayor   **d.** dictator

_____ **9. caste**   **a.** class   **b.** strength   **c.** power   **d.** intelligence

_____ **10. chariot**   **a.** wheel   **b.** fireplace   **c.** cart   **d.** ruler

EXERCISE 5: Determine True/False

On the line before each statement, write *T* if the statement is true. Write *F* if it is false. Use your knowledge of the boldfaced target words to help you decide.

_____ **1.** A **chariot** was a coal-powered vehicle.

_____ **2.** A **pharaoh** was the ruler of the Chinese **empire**.

_____ **3.** Something is **sacred** if it has religious value.

_____ **4.** A **pyramid** was an ancient Egyptian home.

_____ **5.** When one people tried to **invade** another, the purpose was often **conquest**.

_____ **6.** The **reign** of a **tyrant** was a period of joy for those he or she ruled.

_____ **7.** A desk used by George Washington would be an **antique** now.

_____ **8.** People in traditional Hindu society were born into a certain **caste**.

_____ **9.** A typical medieval **pageant** included dancing horses, colored lights, and cotton candy.

_____ **10.** A **tyrant** can usually be voted out of office.

UNIT 5

II. Vocabulary Challenge

EXERCISE 6: Speaking

Discuss one of the following topics with a small group of your classmates. Use at least three target words in your discussion.

1. Describe a movie you saw or a book you read that was set in ancient times.

2. Discuss what you know about ancient Egypt.

EXERCISE 7: Word Play

Use the clues to fill in this crossword with the target words.

Across

2. Holy
4. Valuable object
5. Pattern of social classes in Hinduism
6. King Tut's tomb
8. Kingdom
9. Ruler with an iron fist

Down

1. Ruler of old
3. Victory
5. Horse-drawn vehicle
6. Medieval show
7. Overrun
10. It sounds like *rain*

Wordsmart: Etymology

Antique comes from the Latin word *ante*, which means "before." *Ante-* is sometimes used as a prefix in English words. For example, an *antecedent* is something that occurs before something else. Your *antecedents* are your ancestors because they were born before you.

UNIT 5

LESSON 19 Roots and Affixes II

Target Words	Prefixes	Roots	Suffixes
compel, v.	com- ("with")	pel ("drive; push")	
compelling, adj.	com- ("with")	pel ("drive; push")	-ing (creates a participle that acts as an adjective)
expel, v.	ex- ("out")	pel/puls ("drive, push")	
expulsion, n.	ex- ("out")	pel/puls ("drive, push")	-ion ("act or state of")
impulse, n.	im- ("in; into")	puls ("drive; push")	
impulsive, adj.	im- ("in; into")	puls ("drive; push")	-ive ("tending to be")
inject, v.	in- ("in; into")	ject ("throw")	
injection, n.	in- ("in; into")	ject ("throw")	-ion ("act or state of")
reject, v.	re- ("back")	ject ("throw")	
rejection, n.	re- ("back")	ject ("throw")	-ion ("act or state of")
repel, v.	re- ("back")	pel ("drive; push")	
subject, n.	sub- ("under")	ject ("throw")	

GETTING STARTED

When you come across an unfamiliar word, analyze its parts to determine its meaning. Suppose, for example, that the word *rejection* in this sentence is unfamiliar:

Al wanted his poems published and was upset by the magazine's **rejection** of them.

When you break down the word *rejection,* it appears to mean "the act or state of throwing back":

re- ("back") + *ject* ("throw") + *-ion* ("act or state of")

The context in which the word appears can give you more clues to its meaning. In this sentence, what is "thrown back" is Al's poetry, which the magazine has decided not to publish. So *rejection* means "the act of having your efforts thrown back at you, or refused."

I. Practice the Words

EXERCISE 1: Understand Roots and Affixes

Complete each word tree by adding the appropriate target words to the different "branches" of the root.

compelling 2. _____ 3. _____ injection 5. _____

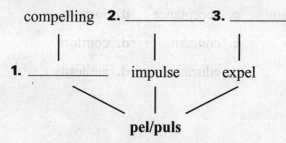

1. _____ impulse expel

pel/puls

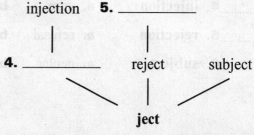

4. _____ reject subject

ject

UNIT 5

EXERCISE 2: Analyze Word Parts and Meanings

Break down each target word into its root and affixes. Then use the parts to help you define the word. The first one is done as an example.

1. Maura rolled up her sleeve for an **injection** of flu vaccine from the nurse.

   (affix) ___*in*___ + (root) ___*ject*___ + (affix) ___*-ion*___

   meaning: *the act of putting something, usually medicine, into the body with a needle.*

2. Paul is an **impulsive** shopper, buying unnecessary things that catch his eye.

   (affix) _____ + (root) _____ + (affix) _____

   meaning: _____

3. Global warming is a **compelling** problem that demands our full attention.

   (affix) _____ + (root) _____ + (affix) _____

   meaning: _____

4. Will officials **expel** Leona for bad behavior, or will she be allowed back in school?

   (affix) _____ + (root) _____

   meaning: _____

5. Would the president accept their advice, or would he **reject** it?

   (affix) _____ + (root) _____

   meaning: _____

6. As a loyal **subject** of Queen Alice, Sir Daniel obeyed all her commands.

   (affix) _____ + (root) _____

   meaning: _____

EXERCISE 3: Identify Synonyms

On the line before each item, write the letter of the word that is closest in meaning to the boldfaced target word. Use your knowledge of word parts to help you.

_____ **1. compel**   **a.** force   **b.** ignore   **c.** disturb   **d.** bring

_____ **2. expel**   **a.** believe   **b.** invite   **c.** remove   **d.** punish

_____ **3. impulse**   **a.** value   **b.** rhythm   **c.** relaxation   **d.** urge

_____ **4. injection**   **a.** cure   **b.** vaccination   **c.** acceptance   **d.** sorrow

_____ **5. rejection**   **a.** refusal   **b.** intensity   **c.** concern   **d.** comfort

_____ **6. subject**   **a.** center   **b.** topic   **c.** education   **d.** authority

EXERCISE 4: Identify Antonyms

On the line before each item, write the letter of the word that is most nearly the opposite of the boldfaced target word. Use your knowledge of word parts to help you.

_____ **1. compelling**   **a.** fascinating   **b.** boring   **c.** forceful   **d.** demanding

_____ **2. expulsion**   **a.** belief   **b.** mention   **c.** invitation   **d.** loss

_____ **3. impulsive**   **a.** puzzling   **b.** planned   **c.** spontaneous   **d.** merry

_____ **4. inject**   **a.** insert   **b.** strain   **c.** remove   **d.** reveal

_____ **5. reject**   **a.** press   **b.** influence   **c.** please   **d.** accept

_____ **6. repel**   **a.** divide   **b.** worry   **c.** attract   **d.** destroy

EXERCISE 5: Use Context to Identify Meaning

Use the word parts and context clues such as cause and effect to help you determine the meaning of the boldfaced target word in each sentence. Write the letter of the meaning on the line before the sentence.

_____ **1.** Afraid that her speech was boring, Sonja tried to **inject** some humor into it.
　　a. throw in   **c.** laugh at
　　b. heal   **d.** pierce

_____ **2.** The companies kept polluting, so the state passed a law to **compel** them to stop.
　　a. reward   **c.** convince
　　b. force   **d.** ask politely

_____ **3.** Larry did not ask any girls to dance because he was afraid of **rejection.**
　　a. the act of inviting   **c.** the act of hurting
　　b. the act of refusing   **d.** the act of dancing

_____ **4.** Although Monica was dieting, she had an **impulse** to eat a rich dessert.
　　a. a troubled mind   **c.** a good reason
　　b. a sense of purpose   **d.** a sudden urge

_____ **5.** Bad behavior resulted in Leo's **expulsion** from the school.
　　a. the act of stretching   **c.** the act of forcing out
　　b. the act of attending   **d.** the act of graduating

_____ **6.** The gardener used a garlic spray to **repel** the deer that were eating the flowers.
　　a. drive off   **c.** confuse
　　b. trap   **d.** feed

II. Vocabulary Challenge

EXERCISE 6: Use Target Words in Writing

On a separate sheet of paper, write a paragraph about a time when you had an urge to do something silly. Use at least three target words in your paragraph.

EXERCISE 7: Create Your Own Words

For each root below, add an affix from this lesson to form a word. Then use the word in a sentence. You may use a dictionary if needed.

> **Prefixes:** *com-* ("with"), *ex-* ("out"), *im-*, *in-* ("in; into"),
> *re-* ("back"), *sub-* ("under")
>
> **Suffixes:** *-ing*, (creates a participle that acts as an adjective),
> *-ion* ("act or state of"), *-ive* ("tending to be")

1. *pend/pens* (hang, weigh, pay) _____

_____

2. *form* (shape)   _____

_____

3. *plor* (cry out)   _____

_____

4. *tract* (pull, move)   _____

_____

EXERCISE 8: Extend Your Vocabulary

Use the clues to help you complete the words below, which have the same roots as the target words. Fill in the missing letters in each word with one of the affixes listed here. You can use an affix more than once, but be sure to use all of the affixes.

> **Prefixes:** *dis-* ("absence of") *inter-* ("between") *pro-* ("before; in front of")
> **Suffixes:** *-or* ("one who performs an action")

EXAMPLE   to drive forward   _p_ _r_ _o_ **p e l**

1. a machine that throws images onto a screen   ___ ___ ___ ___ **j e c t** ___ ___

2. to drive away; to scatter   ___ ___ ___ **p e l**

3. to throw your voice forward   ___ ___ ___ **j e c t**

4. to interrupt by throwing in a remark   ___ ___ ___ ___ ___ **j e c t**

> ### Wordsmart: Spelling
>
> With no suffix after it, the root *pel* is spelled with just one *l*: compel, expel, repel. However, when you add a suffix that starts with a vowel to the root *pel*, double the *l*: compel + -ing = compelling, expel + -ed = expelled, repel + -ent = repellent.

LESSON 20 Words Used in Social Studies

Target Words

architecture, *n.* the art or science of designing and constructing buildings and other structures; the buildings and structures in a particular time or place

citizen, *n.* a person living in a country, state, city, or town who is entitled to its rights and subject to its laws

civic, *adj.* relating to towns and cities; relating to being a citizen

commerce, *n.* the buying and selling of goods, especially on a large scale; trade

community, *n.* a group of people who live in the same area or have common interests

culture, *n.* the ideas, customs, skills, and arts of a people, a group, or a nation

democracy, *n.* a system of government in which the people rule directly or through elected representatives

dictatorship, *n.* a government ruled by a person or group with unlimited power

economy, *n.* the system or group of activities involving the wealth and resources of a household, a community, a region, or a nation

justice, *n.* fairness; the upholding of what is lawful

political, *adj.* relating to matters of government or the state

republic, *n.* a nation in which power rests with citizens who vote for representatives

GETTING STARTED

Social studies explores the world of the past and the way we live today. It has a specialized vocabulary related to government, business, current events, and other areas of daily life. Learning the vocabulary can help you better understand the social studies you learn in school. It can also improve your writing and speaking skills by giving you more words to describe the world around you.

I. Practice the Words

EXERCISE 1: Solve a Paragraph Puzzle

In each pair of parentheses in the paragraph, circle the target word that best fits the sentence. Use your knowledge of paragraph clues to help you make your choices.

Our city is having financial problems. Yesterday, the mayor unveiled a plan to

strengthen its (culture, economy). Her idea is to increase (commerce, justice) by

attracting more businesses to the city. She also wants to beautify the downtown

area by constructing new buildings that have a modern style of (community,

architecture). Because she is acting without consulting anyone in the (culture,

community), people feel as if they are living in a (democracy, dictatorship).

"Our city has a unique (culture, republic) that blends the ideas, customs,

and skills of different groups of people," said local (political, citizen) Ralph

Hopkins, a 30-year resident of the city. "Those ideas need to be heard."

EXERCISE 2: Match Ideas to Context

Using your knowledge of the boldfaced target words and sentence clues, choose the answer that best completes each statement. Write the letter of your choice on the line in the statement.

1. If you were interested in **political** matters, you probably would study _____.
   a. law   **b.** literature   **c.** medicine   **d.** algebra

2. Treating other people with **justice** means _____.
   a. criticizing them   **b.** being fair to them   **c.** leading them   **d.** advising them

3. An important part of a nation's **economy** is its _____.
   a. banking system   **b.** music and dance   **c.** schools   **d.** architecture

4. People living in a **democracy** have _____.
   a. a king or queen   **b.** only one child   **c.** new cars   **d.** the right to vote

5. The **culture** of a nation includes its _____.
   a. waterways   **b.** arts   **c.** climate   **d.** agriculture

6. People in a **community** are usually _____.
   a. closely connected   **b.** well educated   **c.** far apart   **d.** the same age

7. Someone studying **architecture** would learn a lot about _____.
   a. fashion   **b.** buildings   **c.** farming   **d.** language

8. Being a **citizen** of a country entitles you to _____.
   a. legal protections   **b.** an easy life   **c.** a home   **d.** a good job

9. If you lived in a **dictatorship**, you probably would not have _____.
   a. laws   **b.** money   **c.** family   **d.** freedom of speech

10. People living in a **republic** have _____.
    a. political representation   **b.** religious leaders   **c.** a king   **d.** weak laws

11. Your **civic** responsibility is a responsibility to your _____.
    a. self   **b.** city or town   **c.** family   **d.** religious faith

12. Most of a town's **commerce** takes place in _____.
    a. offices and stores   **b.** schools   **c.** courts   **d.** residential areas

EXERCISE 3: Determine True/False

On the line before each statement, write *T* if the statement is true. Write *F* if it is false. Use your knowledge of the boldfaced target words to help you decide.

_____ 1. **Civic** matters have to do with a city and its residents.

_____ 2. People living under a **dictatorship** have a lot of freedom.

_____ 3. In a **democracy,** people can vote to have their say in the government.

_____ 4. In a **republic,** no one can question or give advice to the person who rules.

UNIT 5

EXERCISE 4: Analyze Word Relationships

Each question below contains one boldfaced target word. On the lines provided, answer
the question with a statement that accurately uses the target word in parentheses.

EXAMPLE   What is a **dictatorship** like?

(**democracy**) *Instead of having democracy, people in a dictatorship are ruled
by a person or group with unlimited power.*

1. How might a **citizen** view his or her city?

(**civic**) _____

_____

2. What are some aspects of **culture?**

(**architecture**) _____

_____

3. How can **commerce** help revive a city?

(**economy**) _____

_____

4. What kind of **democracy** is the United States?

(**republic**) _____

_____

5. What does a **political** activist try to achieve?

(**community**) _____

_____

6. Are most people treated fairly in a **dictatorship?**

(**justice**) _____

_____

EXERCISE 5: Use Target Words in Writing

On a separate sheet of paper, write a paragraph about daily life in your city or town.
Use at least three target words in your paragraph.

II. Vocabulary Challenge

EXERCISE 6: Speaking

Discuss one of the following topics with a small group of your classmates. Use at least three target words in your discussion.

1. Describe a recent election that took place in your city or state.

2. Discuss recent or future improvements to your town, city, or region.

EXERCISE 7: Word Play

Use the clues to figure out which target word to put on the lines after each clue. Put one letter on each line. Then put the letters that are on the numbered lines into the boxes with the corresponding numbers. When you are done, the letters in the boxes should spell out something you learn about in social studies. An example is done to get you started.

1	2	3	■	4	5	6	7	8	9	10	11	■	12	13	14	15	16	17	18	19	20	21

1. Business and trade are part of it e c o n o m y (5)

2. Someone who can vote ___ ___ ___ ___(19) ___ ___ ___(21)

3. "With liberty and _____ for all" ___ ___ ___ ___(18) ___ ___ ___ ___

4. The arts and sciences ___ ___ ___(17) ___ ___ ___ ___(13) ___ ___

5. Voting is a citizen's _____ duty ___ ___ ___(14) ___ ___

6. Rule by a tyrant ___ ___ ___(10) ___ ___ ___ ___ ___(2) ___ ___ ___

7. The U.S. has two main _____ parties ___ ___ ___(20) ___ ___ ___ ___(8) ___ ___

8. "And to the _____ for which it stands" ___(7) ___ ___ ___ ___ ___ ___(16) ___ ___

9. Trade between cities or nations ___ ___ ___(15) ___ ___ ___ ___(12) ___ ___ ___

10. Buildings and bridges are part of it ___ ___(9) ___ ___ ___ ___ ___(6) ___ ___ ___ ___ ___

11. Government of, by, and for the people ___ ___(3) ___ ___ ___ ___(4) ___ ___ ___

12. Where people live together ___ ___ ___ ___ ___(11) ___(1) ___ ___

Wordsmart: Etymology

Dictatorship contains the Latin root *dict,* meaning "say." A *dictator* is someone who says what everyone in the nation must do. The nation that he or she rules is called a *dictatorship.* The root *dict* occurs in many other English words. To *predict,* for instance, is to say in advance what will happen; *diction* refers to the way you speak, and a *dictionary* tells you how to say (or write) words.

Check Your Knowledge: Unit 5

By now you have added 48 new words to your vocabulary. Test your ability to use these words in the following exercises.

A. Determine Meaning from Context

On the line before each sentence, write the letter of the word or phrase that is closest in meaning to the boldfaced target word. Use context clues and your knowledge of roots and affixes to help you decide.

_____ 1. Numbers showing the **expiration** are stamped on every container of milk.
    a. starting date   **b.** ending date   **c.** price   **d.** quantity

_____ 2. Breaking the rules of the club can result in your **expulsion.**
    a. membership   **b.** loss of privileges   **c.** removal   **d.** injury

_____ 3. Her slide show was so **uninspiring** that the audience fell asleep.
    a. not exciting   **b.** not original   **c.** not true   **d.** not complete

_____ 4. The rose festival is a beautiful **pageant** held each year in our city.
    a. showy display   **b.** part of a garden   **c.** long hike   **d.** old custom

_____ 5. Will you attend the contest as a **spectator,** or will you join the fun?
    a. scorekeeper   **b.** onlooker   **c.** team   **d.** contestant

_____ 6. The **tyrant** had people jailed just for criticizing his leadership.
    a. palace guard   **b.** elected official   **c.** guard   **d.** harsh ruler

_____ 7. It is hard to **compel** people to do something they do not want to do.
    a. limit   **b.** beg   **c.** force   **d.** expect

_____ 8. During the **reign** of the first Queen Elizabeth, England became a world power.
    a. time of war   **b.** period of rule   **c.** throne   **d.** dictatorship

_____ 9. Soldier and explorer Hernando Cortés led the Spanish **conquest** of Mexico.
    a. victory over   **b.** study of   **c.** voyage to   **d.** improvement of

_____ 10. Shari is a well-behaved child who speaks **respectfully** to older people.
    a. in a calm way   **b.** in a happy way   **c.** in a sad way   **d.** in a polite way

B. Identify Synonyms

On the line before each item, write the letter of the word that is closest in meaning to the boldfaced target word.

_____ **1. inspect**   **a.** squint   **b.** respond   **c.** examine   **d.** ignore

_____ **2. reign**   **a.** elect   **b.** rule   **c.** organize   **d.** whip

_____ **3. sacred**   **a.** holy   **b.** lost   **c.** valuable   **d.** mysterious

_____ **4. tyrant**   **a.** hero   **b.** owner   **c.** president   **d.** dictator

_____ **5. justice**   **a.** fairness   **b.** happiness   **c.** belief   **d.** crime

_____ **6. expect**   **a.** believe   **b.** create   **c.** await   **d.** perform

_____ **7. commerce**   **a.** building   **b.** trade   **c.** politics   **d.** waterway

C. Identify Antonyms

On the line before each item, write the letter of the word that is most nearly the opposite of the boldfaced target word.

_____ **1. expire**   **a.** start   **b.** die   **c.** close   **d.** retire

_____ **2. respectfully** **a.** blindly   **b.** loudly   **c.** kindly   **d.** rudely

_____ **3. impulsive**   **a.** careless   **b.** generous   **c.** hesitant   **d.** greedy

_____ **4. rejection**   **a.** criticism   **b.** confusion   **c.** loss   **d.** acceptance

_____ **5. conquest**   **a.** triumph   **b.** defeat   **c.** wisdom   **d.** foolishness

_____ **6. subject**   **a.** warrior   **b.** servant   **c.** challenger   **d.** ruler

_____ **7. expel**   **a.** occur   **b.** mix   **c.** invite   **d.** catch

D. Match Ideas

On the line before each item, write the letter of the target word that most clearly relates to the situation in the sentence. Use each word only once.

a. architecture	**b.** culture	**c.** compelling	**d.** economy
e. impulse	**f.** inspection	**g.** inspiration	**h.** political

_____ **1.** A city worker is coming to make sure the restaurant is clean.

_____ **2.** Seeing Van Gogh's paintings made me want to paint too.

_____ **3.** Downtown Chicago is noted for its interesting skyscrapers.

_____ **4.** The book is a great read; I could not put it down.

_____ **5.** The candidates campaigned to win the election.

_____ **6.** It was not on my shopping list, but I could not resist it and bought it anyway.

_____ **7.** The museum offers lectures on art, music, literature, and history.

_____ **8.** The study focused on the wealth and resources of the nation.

E. Determine True/False

On the line before each statement, write *T* if the statement is true. Write *F* if it is false. Use your knowledge of the boldfaced target words to help you decide.

_____ **1.** The ruler of a **dictatorship** is often a **tyrant.**

_____ **2.** An **empire** is usually smaller than a nation.

_____ **3.** A **pharaoh** was often buried in a **pyramid.**

_____ **4.** To be valuable, an **antique** must be brand new.

_____ **5.** In a **republic,** people elect others to represent them.

_____ **6.** In a **democracy,** a **citizen** has a voice in the government.

_____ **7.** Taking a **chariot** to another city would be faster than going by car.

UNIT 5

F. Analyze Roots and Affixes

For each word, show how the meaning of its parts reflects the meaning of the word.

EXAMPLE **expect**   ex- ("out") + spect ("look; see") = expect, "to look out for; to think likely to happen; to await"

1. inspector: _____

_____

2. injection: _____

_____

3. reject: _____

_____

4. inspirational: _____

_____

5. repel: _____

_____

G. Use Words in Context

Choose the target word below that best completes each sentence, and write it on the line provided. Use each target word only once. Not all the target words will be used.

civic   community   expectation   expiration
impulsive   inject   invade   caste

1. The army crossed the border to _____ the neighboring nation.

2. The nurse used a syringe to _____ the medicine into my arm.

3. It is a person's _____ duty to serve on a jury when asked.

4. Shopkeepers in Hindu society would be members of the merchant _____.

5. People in the _____ asked the town council for a new library.

6. I planned the day with the _____ that you would be on time, but I was wrong.

UNIT 5

LESSON 22 Words Related to Travel

Target Words

arrival, *n.* the act of reaching a place

brochure, *n.* a pamphlet used to explain, promote, or advertise something

currency, *n.* the money used in a country

departure, *n.* the act of leaving a place

destination, *n.* a place to which someone is traveling or being sent

detour, *n., v.* a route used temporarily instead of a main route; to go by a roundabout way

elevation, *n.* the height above sea level

itinerary, *n.* a detailed plan for a proposed trip; a route or proposed route of a trip; a record of a trip

landmark, *n.* a prominent feature in a landscape; a building or site with historical significance

legend, *n.* a short description or key that explains the symbols on a map

passport, *n.* a government document that certifies a person's identity and citizenship and permits him or her to travel abroad

terrain, *n.* an area of land; ground; the surface features of an area of land

GETTING STARTED

The words in this lesson are used to describe travels and travel arrangements. They will help you understand stories and essays about travel that you may read for school or pleasure.

I. Practice the Words

EXERCISE 1: Solve a Paragraph Puzzle

Using the target words and your knowledge of context clues such as restatement, fill in all the blank spaces in the paragraph. Use each word only once. Be sure the words fit grammatically into the sentences.

Our train trip began with a morning _____ from Denver. The explanation

on our map's _____, or key, indicated that we would go through tunnels

as we climbed to a higher _____ to cross the Rocky Mountains. After a

stop in Glenwood Springs, we rode along the Colorado River, a prominent feature in the

_____ and a well-known _____. The next day, after a short

_____ to avoid some damaged track, we reached Sacramento, the first stop

on our _____, or route. After a bus tour to Yosemite Park, we pushed on

to our final _____ of Vancouver, Canada. I brought a _____

to cross the border into Canada, a tourist _____, and some Canadian

_____ to pay for a taxi upon our _____ in Vancouver.

UNIT 6

EXERCISE 2: Match Ideas to Context

Choose the target word that best completes each statement. Write the letter of your choice on the line in the statement.

1. A monument is one type of _____.
   a. brochure   **b.** currency   **c.** landmark   **d.** passport

2. "Leave San Antonio 10 a.m." would most likely be listed on a traveler's _____.
   a. currency   **b.** destination   **c.** passport   **d.** itinerary

3. The place you are going to is your _____.
   a. arrival   **b.** departure   **c.** destination   **d.** itinerary

4. To find out what symbols on a map mean, look at the _____.
   a. currency   **b.** detour   **c.** legend   **d.** terrain

5. The number of feet above sea level is the _____.
   a. elevation   **b.** landmark   **c.** legend   **d.** terrain

6. Someone picking you up at the airport needs to know your time of _____.
   a. arrival   **b.** currency   **c.** destination   **d.** detour

7. You might add miles to your route if you have to take a _____.
   a. brochure   **b.** detour   **c.** legend   **d.** terrain

8. Before traveling abroad, a U.S. citizen must obtain a _____ from the government.
   a. currency   **b.** detour   **c.** brochure   **d.** passport

9. In a hotel lobby you will often find a _____ advertising a local tourist attraction.
   a. brochure   **b.** destination   **c.** legend   **d.** landmark

10. For foreign travel, you may need to be at the airport two hours before your time of _____.
   a. arrival   **b.** departure   **c.** destination   **d.** elevation

EXERCISE 3: Use Target Words in Writing

On a separate sheet of paper, write a sentence about travel for each of the target words listed at the beginning of this lesson. Be sure your sentences show that you know what the words mean.

EXAMPLE   **passport**   *We showed our passport at the border crossing.*

EXERCISE 4: Identify Synonyms

On the line before each item, write the letter of the choice that is closest in meaning to the boldfaced target word.

_____ 1. **brochure**   a. poster   b. pamphlet   c. magazine   d. ornament

_____ 2. **currency**   a. money   b. documents   c. plans   d. memories

_____ 3. **departure**   a. greeting   b. purpose   c. exit   d. homecoming

_____ 4. **landmark**   a. horizon   b. roadway   c. monument   d. tourist

_____ 5. **elevation**   a. trail   b. height   c. scenery   d. valley

_____ 6. **itinerary**   a. route   b. suitcase   c. ticket   d. identification

_____ 7. **legend**   a. border   b. mileage   c. coloring   d. key

_____ 8. **terrain**   a. rainfall   b. wildlife   c. landscape   d. climate

_____ 9. **passport**   a. document   b. fee   c. photo   d. pledge

_____ 10. **detour**   a. delay   b. route   c. traffic   d. luggage

EXERCISE 5: Determine True/False

On the line before each statement, write *T* if the statement is true. Write *F* if it is false. Use your knowledge of the boldfaced target words to help you decide.

_____ 1. On **arrival** at their **destination**, air travelers can pick up their luggage at the baggage claim area.

_____ 2. A **passport** is a type of **brochure** that advertises a visit to a country.

_____ 3. The Statue of Liberty is a famous **landmark.**

_____ 4. It is difficult to hike over rocky **terrain.**

_____ 5. An **itinerary** would include books to read and music to listen to while traveling.

_____ 6. The **legend** shows which color on the map indicates areas of higher **elevation.**

_____ 7. The dollar, the pound, and the yen are all forms of **currency.**

_____ 8. People in a hurry usually are happy to take a **detour.**

II. Vocabulary Challenge

EXERCISE 6: Speaking

Discuss one of the following topics with a small group of your classmates. Use at least three target words in your discussion.

1. Describe a trip you took or hope to take.

2. Discuss the travels of a character in a book you read or a film you saw.

EXERCISE 7: Word Play

Unscramble each cluster of scrambled letters to form a different target word. Write the target words on the lines provided. Use the clues in parentheses to help you figure out the target words.

1. dmklraan _____ (the Eiffel Tower is one)

2. ienitnsdato _____ (where you end up)

3. variarl _____ (the act of reaching the place where you are going)

4. edenlg _____ (it decodes the markings on a map)

5. sapoprts _____ (it shows your picture)

6. redotu _____ (a roundabout way)

7. oucbrerh _____ (synonym of *leaflet*)

8. prruaeedt _____ (antonym of *arrival*)

9. creruync _____ (coins and paper money)

10. telenovia _____ (height above sea level)

11. niteyairr _____ (a trip plan)

12. ienrart _____ (it includes an area's hills, lakes, and forests)

Wordsmart: Etymology

Terrain is from the Latin word *terra,* meaning "earth." As the Latin root *terr,* it appears in several other English words, including *territory,* "an area of land"; *subterranean,* "underground"; *terrace,* "a raised mound of earth with a flat top"; and even *terrier,* a dog that was originally bred to hunt small animals low on the ground. English speakers also use a Latin expression that contains the word *terra: terra firma,* which means "solid ground," as in "The astronaut was glad to be back on terra firma."

LESSON
23 Compound Words

Target Words	Meaning
daredevil, *n., adj.*	someone who boldly performs dangerous feats; recklessly bold
hard drive, *n.*	the main storage area on a computer, which houses the hard disks on which the data is stored
liftoff, *n.*	the initial movement with which, or instant at which, a rocket, a helicopter, or another vehicle leaves the ground
lighthouse, *n.*	a tall structure with a powerful light that aids ships in sailing
roller coaster, *n.*	an amusement park ride in which a small railway travels at high speed up and down hills and around sharp curves
runner-up, *n.*	someone who does not win or who comes in second
shipwreck, *n., v.*	the destruction of a ship or boat; the remains of a destroyed ship or boat; to cause a ship or boat to be destroyed
sister-in-law, *n.*	the sister of one's spouse, wife of one's brother, or wife of one's spouse's brother
sleepwalk, *v.*	to walk while one is asleep
spacecraft, *n.*	a vehicle designed to travel in outer space
sunrise, *n.*	the first appearance of the sun on the horizon; dawn
waterfront, *n.*	land that abuts the water, especially in an area where ships dock

GETTING STARTED

A **base word** is a word that can stand alone. A **compound word** is made of two or more base words that are used together to name a single object, idea, action, or quality. A compound word may be written as one word, a hyphenated word, or separate words. Breaking an unfamiliar compound word into its base words can help you figure out its meaning. For example, suppose you are uncertain of the meaning of *liftoff* in this sentence:

> Everyone watched the exciting moment when the space shuttle achieved *liftoff*.

If you think about the meaning of *lift*, "to raise or rise," and *off*, "no longer on," and consider the context in which *liftoff* is used, you can figure out that the compound word probably means "the movement with which, or the point at which, an air or space vehicle rises from the ground."

I. Practice the Words

EXERCISE 1: Understand Compound Words

Put boxes around the base words in the compound words below. Then use the base words to define the compound words.

roller coaster: _____

lighthouse: _____

EXERCISE 2: Identify Compound Words in Context

Underline each compound word in the paragraph and put a line between the base words it contains. Then, on the lines below the paragraph, write the compound word, its base words, and its meaning. Use sentence clues to help you define the words. An example is done for you.

Last summer we stayed in a motel on the <u>water|front</u>. I woke early every day to see the sunrise behind the lighthouse. Once my sister-in-law took me to a park where rides were set up. My favorite was a roller coaster that was so high, I felt like a daredevil riding it. I also liked the imaginary spacecraft operated by a man dressed like an astronaut who yelled "Liftoff!" each time the ride began. Once there was a contest to see who could build the best structures out of sand. The winner built a castle, but the first runner-up built a crazy boat that looked like a shipwreck on the beach.

1. _waterfront (water + front): land facing the water, especially in the area where ships dock_

2. _____

3. _____

4. _____

5. _____

6. _____

7. _____

8. _____

9. _____

10. _____

EXERCISE 3: Identify Synonyms and Antonyms

For each item below, a boldfaced target word is paired with another word. On the lline before each pair, write *S* if the two words are synonyms. Write *A* if they are antonyms.

_____ 1. **runner-up**/second place   _____ 4. **daredevil**/coward

_____ 2. **sunrise**/dawn   _____ 5. **liftoff**/landing

_____ 3. **spacecraft**/rocket ship   _____ 6. **waterfront**/shoreline

EXERCISE 4: Match Words to Context

Choose the target word that best completes each sentence and write it on the line provided. Use each target word only once. Not all target words will be used.

daredevil	lighthouse	shipwreck	spacecraft
hard drive	roller coaster	sister-in-law	sunrise
liftoff	runner-up	sleepwalk	waterfront

1. If your _____ breaks, your computer will not operate.

2. If you _____, you might wake up in the middle of the night standing in your kitchen.

3. In 1969, Apollo 11, with three astronauts on board, became the first manned _____ to land on the moon.

4. After _____, the rocket ship climbed slowly into the sky.

5. The person who takes second place in a contest is called the _____.

6. Even a _____ should wear a helmet when performing dangerous stunts.

7. When they got married, my brother and _____ bought a house in the city.

8. The most popular ride at the amusement park is a high-speed _____ with heart-stopping curves.

EXERCISE 5: Determine True/False

On the line before each statement, write *T* if the statement is true. Write *F* if it is false. Use your knowledge of the boldfaced target words to help you decide.

_____ 1. A **lighthouse** can help prevent a **shipwreck.**

_____ 2. **Liftoff** occurs when a **spacecraft** lands.

_____ 3. Information on a computer is stored in the **hard drive.**

_____ 4. In April in most places, **sunrise** takes place around 7 P.M.

_____ 5. In a restaurant on the **waterfront,** you might see boats outside the window.

_____ 6. A **daredevil** is someone who is mean and cruel.

_____ 7. People expect a **roller coaster** to move slowly.

_____ 8. Your **sister-in-law** is your relative by marriage, not by birth.

II. Vocabulary Challenge

EXERCISE 6: Use Target Words in Writing

On a separate sheet of paper, write a paragraph about sights you might see while walking along a beach. Use at least three target words in your paragraph.

EXERCISE 7: Extend Your Vocabulary

Add one or more words to each word below to form a compound word. Then define the word you formed.

EXAMPLE   blue*berry*:   *a small, round fruit with a dark blue color*

1. self _____ : _____

2. _____ ball : _____

3. lightning _____ : _____

4. book _____ : _____

5. ice _____ : _____

6. high _____ : _____

7. _____ storm : _____

8. sun _____ : _____

9. paper _____ : _____

10. _____ paper : _____

Wordsmart: Spelling

To form the plural of most compound words, make the final base word plural: *shipwrecks, great-aunts, roller coasters*. For some hyphenated or two-word compounds in which the final base word is not the key word, make an earlier word plural if it is a noun: *runners-up, sisters-in-law, attorneys general*. When in doubt, check a dictionary. If the plural is formed in an unusual way, the dictionary will show it in the listing for the term.

LESSON 24 # Words About the Weather

Target Words
altitude, *n.* the height of something above sea level or above the earth's surface
arctic, *n., adj.* (often capitalized) the region around the North Pole; relating to the North Pole or the area around it; bitter cold
atmosphere, *n.* the air or other gases around a planet or star
balmy, *adj.* pleasant and mild
drench, *v.* to wet completely; to soak
evaporate, *v.* to change from a solid or a liquid into a gas; to draw moisture from; to disappear
forecast, *n., v.* a prediction of what will happen; to predict what will happen
humid, *adj.* full of water vapor; moist
polar, *adj.* relating to the North or South Pole
precipitation, *n.* any form of water such as rain, snow, sleet, or hail that falls to the earth's surface
sleet, *n.* frozen or partly frozen rain
slush, *n.* partly melted snow or ice on the ground

GETTING STARTED

The words in this lesson are about weather in all its forms. These words are the specialized vocabulary of weather reports and science texts. Knowledge of these words will help you be more precise in talking or writing about the weather and other science topics.

I. Practice the Words

EXERCISE 1: Solve a Paragraph Puzzle

Circle the target word in parentheses that best completes each sentence in the paragraph. Use sentence clues to help you decide.

Near the top of the mountain, the (altitude, atmosphere) was thinner than it

was down below. Today was so (arctic, humid), however, that the air felt thick

with moisture even at this high (altitude, precipitation). A (balmy, polar) breeze

blew, pleasantly warm on our skins. Yet the weather (forecast, slush) predicted

that today's nice weather would not last. Soon, (precipitation, atmosphere) in

the form of rain or (sleet, slush) would come down from the sky and (drench,

evaporate) the area. Later, a cold front would pass through and bring a blast of

(humid, arctic) air.

EXERCISE 2: Match Ideas to Context

Using your knowledge of the boldfaced target words, choose the answer that best completes each statement. Write the letter of your choice on the line in the statement.

1. The _____ will **drench** the ground and help the crops to grow.
    a. rainfall   b. farm equipment   c. dry weather   d. strong winds

2. Heat can make water **evaporate** into a cloud of _____.
    a. ice   b. snowflakes   c. mud   d. steam

3. You will most likely find a weather **forecast** _____.
    a. at a concert   b. in a store   c. in a textbook   d. on television

4. On a **balmy** day in May, you most likely would wear _____.
    a. heavy boots   b. a rain hat   c. light clothing   d. a thick sweater

5. An **arctic** front usually brings weather that is _____.
    a. frigid   b. humid   c. tropical   d. unpredictable

6. As it falls from the sky, **precipitation** sometimes takes the form of _____.
    a. wind   b. clouds   c. sunshine   d. rain

7. The earth's **atmosphere** is made up mainly of _____.
    a. rocks   b. gases   c. minerals   d. vitamins

8. In its natural habitat, a **polar** bear lives in _____.
    a. a jungle   b. a desert   c. a forest   d. an icy region

9. The **altitude** of a big _____ is usually well over 5,000 feet.
    a. wave   b. mountain   c. desert   d. city

10. On a **humid** day, the air feels heavy and _____.
    a. damp   b. dry   c. thin   d. cold

11. When cars go through watery **slush,** they are likely to _____.
    a. overheat   b. splash   c. speed   d. honk

12. **Sleet** is a form of **precipitation** that consists of _____.
    a. frozen rain   b. thick clouds   c. water vapor   d. deep snow

EXERCISE 3: Identify Synonyms and Antonyms

In each item below, a boldfaced target word is paired with another word. On the line before each pair, write *S* if the two words are synonyms. Write *A* if they are antonyms.

_____ 1. **altitude**/depth

_____ 2. **balmy**/mild

_____ 3. **forecast**/prediction

_____ 4. **precipitation**/drought

_____ 5. **drench**/soak

_____ 6. **humid**/dry

_____ 7. **sleet**/ice

_____ 8. **arctic**/frigid

EXERCISE 4: Determine True/False

Each of the following statements contains at least one boldfaced target word. On the line before the statement, write *T* if it is true. Write *F* if it is false.

_____ 1. **Sleet** is one form of **precipitation.**

_____ 2. Most people prefer to wear new shoes to walk through **slush.**

_____ 3. Heat will **evaporate** water.

_____ 4. An **arctic** wind comes from the region around the North Pole.

_____ 5. A heavy rain can **drench** an area in a short time.

_____ 6. If reports **forecast** a **balmy** day, most people will wear layers of warm clothing.

_____ 7. On a **humid** day, there is moisture in the **atmosphere.**

_____ 8. People living at sea level live at a high **altitude**.

EXERCISE 5: Use Target Words in Writing

On a separate sheet of paper, write a sentence about the weather for each of the target words listed at the beginning of this lesson. Be sure your sentences show that you understand what the words mean.

EXAMPLE   altitude   *At a high altitude, temperatures are often lower.*

II. Vocabulary Challenge

EXERCISE 6: Speaking

Discuss one of the following topics with a small group of your classmates. Use at least three target words in your discussion.

1. Give an imaginary weather report that might be heard on the radio or television.

2. Discuss a time when bad weather ruined your plans.

EXERCISE 7: Word Play

Use the clues to fill in this crossword with the target words

Across

1. You need boots to walk in this icy mixture

4. Gases surrounding Earth

7. Weather prediction

9. 14,000 feet above sea level

12. Extremely cold

Down

2. Wintry rain

3. Pleasant, mild

5. Rain or snow

6. Disappear

8. Bear that likes an icy climate

10. Soak

11. Word to describe a rainforest climate

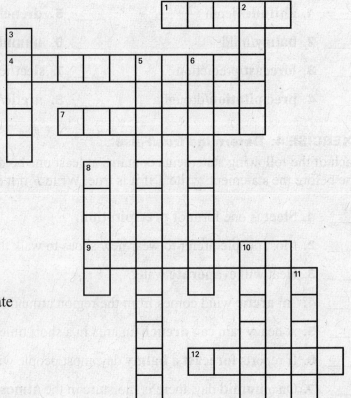

Wordsmart: Etymology

The word *arctic* can be capitalized and used as a noun, as in *the Arctic*, or as part of a proper noun, as in *Arctic Circle* and *Arctic Ocean*. The word comes from the Greek *arktikos,* meaning "bear," because the area around the North Pole falls under the constellation of stars known as the Great Bear. This constellation, in which the stars seem to form the shape of a bear in the nighttime sky, is also known as Ursa Major, Latin for "Great Bear."

Check Your Knowledge: Unit 6

By now you have added 48 new words to your vocabulary. Test your ability to use these words in the following exercises.

A. Determine Meaning from Context

On the line before each sentence, write the letter of the word or phrase that is closest in meaning to the boldfaced target word. Use the context clues to help you decide.

_____ **1.** The snowshoe hare turns white in winter to **camouflage** itself in the snow.

a. to disguise oneself   **c.** to survive

b. to be in danger   **d.** to fight off

_____ **2.** The trip took several hours, but we finally reached our **destination**.

a. a stop along the way   **c.** the place from which a traveler leaves

b. a disappointing visit   **d.** the place to which a traveler goes

_____ **3.** The air gets thinner as you travel to a higher **elevation**.

a. valley   **c.** scenic view

b. desert   **d.** height

_____ **4.** Fisherman's Wharf is a popular place on San Francisco's **waterfront**.

a. area by the water   **c.** ocean wave

b. winter storage area   **d.** swimming pool

_____ **5.** On a hot, **humid** day I perspire more than I do on a hot, dry day.

a. hot   **c.** moist

b. cool   **d.** dry

B. Use Words in Context

Select a target word from the list to complete each sentence and write it on the line provided. Use each word only once. Some words will not be used.

atmosphere	hard drive	daredevil	lighthouse
precipitation	spacecraft	slush	tsunami

1. Will the day be dry, or will there be _____ of some kind?

2. As the day warmed, the snow in the driveway turned to _____.

3. Oxygen and nitrogen are gases that are part of the earth's _____.

4. The ships in which astronauts travel are known as _____.

5. The disks in the _____ contain information that is key to operating the computer.

C. Identify Synonyms

On the line before each item, write the letter of the word that is closest in meaning to the boldfaced target word.

_____ 1. **evaporate**   a. freeze   b. leak   c. divide   d. vanish

_____ 2. **brochure**   a. booklet   b. notebook   c. letter   d. textbook

_____ 3. **paradise**   a. cruise   b. island   c. Eden   d. luck

_____ 4. **balmy**   a. breezy   b. crazy   c. foggy   d. pleasant

_____ 5. **polar**   a. angry   b. windy   c. icy   d. warm

_____ 6. **forecast**   a. summary   b. outlook   c. performance   d. rumor

_____ 7. **drench**   a. wet   b. steam   c. fry   d. force

D. Identify Antonyms

On the line before each item, write the letter of the word that is most nearly the opposite of the boldfaced target word.

_____ 1. **sunrise**   a. dawn   b. morning   c. sunlight   d. sunset

_____ 2. **camouflage**   a. hide   b. expose   c. travel   d. pause

_____ 3. **tycoon**   a. windstorm   b. problem   c. bum   d. leader

_____ 4. **canyon**   a. valley   b. desert   c. peak   d. jungle

_____ 5. **altitude**   a. direction   b. height   c. weight   d. deepness

_____ 6. **humid**   a. solid   b. parched   c. serious   d. bold

_____ 7. **arctic**   a. tropical   b. cloudy   c. frigid   d. distant

UNIT 6

E. Match Ideas

On the line before each item, write the target word from the list below that is most clearly related to the situation described in the sentence. Use each word only once.

confetti   detour   passport   tsunami
currency   liftoff   runner-up

_____ **1.** Arriving in Mexico, we need to change our dollars to pesos.

_____ **2.** In a race, track star Bernardo Baez comes in second.

_____ **3.** The rocket leaves the ground and heads for space.

_____ **4.** People on the parade floats throw bits of paper at the crowd.

_____ **5.** A traveler must take a different route to avoid flooding.

_____ **6.** An underwater earthquake causes a major disturbance in the ocean.

_____ **7.** We show the border guard a document that proves our citizenship.

F. Determine True/False

On the line before the statement, write *T* if the statement is true. Write *F* if it is false. Use your knowledge of the boldfaced target words to help you decide.

_____ **1.** **Sleet** is a form of **precipitation** that occurs in the summer.

_____ **2.** The moment when a **spacecraft** leaves the ground is called the **liftoff.**

_____ **3.** An **itinerary** usually lists times of **arrival** and **departure** for each **destination**.

_____ **4.** An iceberg can cause a **shipwreck.**

_____ **5.** On most maps, the **legend** shows pictures of heroes who explored the **terrain.**

_____ **6.** A **coyote** is larger than an elephant.

_____ **7.** A **landmark** shows the quality of the soil beneath it.

_____ **8.** A scary **roller coaster** might appeal to a **daredevil.**

UNIT 6

G. Identify Foreign Origins

Match the target words on the left to their countries of origin on the right by placing the correct letter on the line after each target word. Use each origin only once.

1. bazaar _____
2. bouquet _____
3. kindergarten _____
4. vista _____
5. waltz _____

a. from the French word for "small bush"

b. from the German word for "children's garden"

c. from the German word for "to turn or twist about"

d. from the Italian word for "sight"

e. from the Persian word for "market"

H. Understand Compound Words

In the space provided, divide each word into its base words; then define it.

1. sleepwalk: _____
   _____

2. landmark: _____
   _____

3. passport: _____
   _____

4. roller coaster: _____
   _____

5. sister-in-law: _____
   _____

6. waterfront: _____
   _____

Feature: Homophones and Homographs

WHAT IS IT?

Homophones are words that sound the same but have different spellings and meanings. For example, the words *see*, meaning "to observe," and *sea*, meaning "the ocean," are homophones. **Homographs** are words that are spelled the same but have different meanings and origins. They may or may not have the same pronunciation. Dictionaries usually list homographs as separately numbered entries. For example:

> **stoop**[1] (Middle English *stoupen*, from Old English *stupian*) *v.* 1 To bend forward and down from the waist. 2 To lower oneself. *n.* A forward bending of the head and back.
>
> **stoop**[2] (Dutch *stoep*, front verandah) *n.* A small porch, platform, or staircase leading to the entrance of a house.

WHY IT MATTERS

Knowing the difference between homophones will help you spell words correctly. Errors with homophones will not be caught by a computer spell checker because the wrong word is still a word, so you need to be your own spell checker.

Knowing the difference between homographs will help you better understand what you read. To decide which homograph applies to a particular situation, study the context, or the surrounding words and sentences.

EXERCISE 1: Identify Homophones

In these sentences, circle the correct homophone from each choice in parentheses. Check your answers in a dictionary.

1. The library had an old (addition, edition) of Carl Sandburg's poems.

2. I asked my advisor to (council, counsel) me about subjects to take in middle school.

3. The (naval, navel) officer and the pilot met in the airplane (hangar, hanger).

4. The (wringing, ringing) of the church bells echoed in the forest of (fir, fur) trees.

5. The weary shoppers walked through the crowded (bizarre, bazaar) in a (days, daze).

6. The workers at the job (sight, site) sent the empty containers down a (chute, shoot).

7. In an amazing (feat, feet), the circus star (pedaled, peddled) a bicycle on the high wire.

8. For each note Laura played on the piano, I played a (chord, cord) on the (base, bass).

9. Members of the (bridle, bridal) party were standing at the (altar, alter).

10. Weehawken, New Jersey, was the (seen, scene) of a famous (dual, duel) in U.S. history.

11. The dog picked a (flee, flea) from its thick, (coarse, course) fur.

12. The king's oldest child was the (heir, air) to the (throne, thrown).

EXERCISE 2: Identify Triple Homophones

Most homophones are pairs, but some are triples. Complete each of the following sentences by circling one of the three answer choices in parentheses.

1. A (vane, vain, vein) carries blood to the heart.

2. The scouts needed an (or, ore, oar) to row the boat.

3. Greece was the (site, cite, sight) of the first Olympic games.

4. He had been living in Texas (fore, for, four) five years.

5. The farmer will (sew, so, sow) the seeds in the spring.

6. A lion (preys, prays, praise) on weaker animals.

7. You need a sharp knife to (pare, pear, pair) an apple.

8. The baby began to (wail, wale, whale) when his mother left the room.

EXERCISE 3: Use Context to Determine Meaning

For each pair of sentences, use context clues to help you decide which meaning on the right applies to each boldfaced homograph. Write the letter of the meaning on the line before the sentence.

1. _____ The bank keeps money in a **vault.**   **A.** to leap over, using hands or a pole

    _____ Olga tried to **vault** over the barrier.   **B.** a secure room or storage area

2. _____ Carl had to **pore** over the test.   **A.** to study or read carefully

    _____ Amy had a clogged **pore** on her chin.   **B.** a tiny opening in skin or leaves

3. _____ Write your story in the past **tense.**   **A.** form of a verb that shows time of action

    _____ People were **tense** during the trial.   **B.** tightly stretched; nervous

4. _____ He cut marble out of the **quarry.**   **A.** something being hunted

    _____ The wolves chased their **quarry.**   **B.** a place where stone is excavated

5. _____ Of the two sisters, Eve is the **elder.**   **A.** born earlier; older

    _____ We sat in the shade of an **elder.**   **B.** a small tree or shrub with berries

6. _____ He got a **rash** from the poison ivy.   **A.** acting without thought

    _____ It would be **rash** to quit your job.   **B.** spots on the skin

7. _____ An expired license is **invalid.**   **A.** person who is sick or weak

    _____ His grandmother is an **invalid.**   **B.** having no force or value

8. _____ What did the plumber **charge**?   **A.** ask as a price for something

    _____ General Grant led the **charge.**   **B.** a forceful attack

LESSON 25 Word Origins: Classical Mythology

Target Words	Current Meaning	Origin in Mythology
amazon, *n.*	a very tall, big, or strong woman	Amazons, Greek female warriors
atlas, *n.*	a book of maps	Atlas, Greek god said to support the heavens on his shoulders
cereal, *n.*	grains such as wheat, oats, or corn that are used as food	Ceres, Roman goddess of agriculture
echo, *n., v.*	a repeated sound that bounces off of a surface; to repeat	Echo, Greek nymph who pined for love and faded away until only her voice remained
fortune, *n.*	luck or fate; good luck; wealth	Fortuna, Roman goddess of luck
furious, *adj.*	full of wild rage; very angry	the Furies, three female spirits who pursued and punished evildoers
museum, *n.*	an institution preserving artistic, historic, or scientific displays	the nine Muses, Greek goddesses of the arts, sciences, and literature
nectar, *n.*	any delicious drink	the drink of the gods
odyssey, *n.*	any long journey or wandering	Odysseus, Greek king who had a long journey home from Troy
Olympian, *adj.*	godlike; majestic	Olympus, Greek mountain said to be the home of the gods
panic, *n., v.*	a sudden, overpowering fear; to feel a sudden, overpowering fear	Pan, Greek nature god said to inspire sudden fear
titanic, *adj.*	very large; gigantic	Titans, a race of giant Greek gods

GETTING STARTED

The mythologies of ancient Greece and Rome have contributed many words to English. The word *echo,* for example, goes back to a Greek myth in which a nymph named Echo loved a handsome young man named Narcissus. When her love was not returned, she wasted away in sadness until only her voice was left, repeating his name over and over. The word *echo* came into common usage with a meaning related to its origin.

I. Practice the Words

EXERCISE 1: Understand Word Origins

Answer these questions based on the mythological origins of English words.

1. What qualities does the name *nectarine* stress about the fruit with that name?

_____

2. Why do you think the famous ship was called the *Titanic?*

_____

EXERCISE 2: Use Words in Context

Using the target words, fill in all the blank spaces in the paragraph. Use each target word only once. Be sure the words fit grammatically into the sentences.

My family lives in a small town in western Pennsylvania, but it is our good _____ to have relatives who live in New York City. Our yearly _____ to visit them begins the day after school ends. While we are there, we usually go to the natural history _____ to see the tools, artwork, and other relics from ancient civilizations. The massive building is a wonder in itself: _____ in its size and _____ in its majestic beauty. This year we plan to get an early start on our trip, so we will have a simple breakfast of cold _____ and a glass of fruit _____. Mom and Dad will share the driving, so they are checking the latest road _____ to agree upon the best way to reach our destination. Last year, we had some nervous moments. Although he is usually calm and even-tempered, Dad was in a _____ because we were late, and he was _____ with my sister for not having the dog ready for the long drive. My sister is thin and delicate, but she has the booming voice of an _____. I could hear Fido's name _____ through the house as she called over and over again for him to come out of his hiding place. This year he is going to stay with my grandparents.

EXERCISE 3: Identify Synonyms and Antonyms

In each item below, a boldfaced target word is paired with another word. On the line before each pair, write *S* if the two words are synonyms. Write *A* if they are antonyms.

_____ **1. fortune**/luck

_____ **2. furious**/pleased

_____ **3. Olympian**/common

_____ **4. amazon**/giant

_____ **5. odyssey**/journey

_____ **6. titanic**/tiny

_____ **7. panic**/calm

_____ **8. echo**/repeat

EXERCISE 4: Apply Meanings to Context

Use your knowledge of prefixes, base words, and sentence clues to help you
determine the meaning of each boldfaced target word below. Write the meaning on
the line after the word.

_____ 1. If a fashion model were called an **amazon,** what would you conclude about her?

    a. She is very tall.   **c.** She wears beautiful clothes.

    b. She is very pretty.   **d.** She has dark hair.

_____ 2. Which sort of home would most likely be called **Olympian?**

    a. a cottage   **c.** an apartment

    b. a shack   **d.** a mansion

_____ 3. What sort of person is likely to **panic?**

    a. a bold person   **c.** a nervous person

    b. a wealthy person   **d.** a wise person

_____ 4. Which of these events would most likely be called an **odyssey?**

    a. a short walk   **c.** a cross-country trip

    b. a day off from school **d.** a one-hour flight

_____ 5. What do people usually do in a **museum?**

    a. view an exhibit   **c.** visit with friends

    b. take a dance class   **d.** study for a test

_____ 6. If you were going on a long trip, why would you use an **atlas?**

    a. to read a story   **c.** to study the route

    b. to learn about the future **d.** to find out the weather

EXERCISE 5: Determine True/False

On the line before each statement below, write *T* if it is true. Write *F* if it is false. Use
your knowledge about the origins of the boldfaced target words to help you answer.

_____ 1. **Nectar** was originally a Roman god with a sweet tooth.

_____ 2. **Olympian,** meaning "majestic," goes back to the Greek gods' mountain home.

_____ 3. **Furious** goes back to Fury, the Roman god of wild horses.

_____ 4. The word **fortune** is related to the name of the Roman goddess of luck.

_____ 5. **Titanic** comes from the Titans, gods who were of giant size.

_____ 6. The word **amazon** comes from the name of a river in ancient Greece.

_____ 7. **Cereal** comes from the name of the Greek god of the morning.

_____ 8. **Odyssey** comes from the name of the Greek king who traveled a long way home.

UNIT 7

II. Vocabulary Challenge

EXERCISE 6: Use Target Words in Writing

On a separate sheet, write a paragraph about a trip you made or plan to make. Use at least three target words in your paragraph.

EXERCISE 7: Word Search

Find and circle each target word hidden in this maze. The words may appear horizontally, vertically, or diagonally. They may be written forward or backward. Different words may overlap and use the same letter.

WORD LIST

amazon	atlas	cereal	echo	fortune	furious
museum	nectar	odyssey	Olympian	panic	titanic

```
N O H C E N P N P V W
O M L B I L E A U F N
Z E K Y A N N C U X A
A I A E M I A R T C F
M R R B C P I T E A O
A E U E W O I A I B R
C M W N U Z J A L T T
Y E S S Y D O T N I U
I R X A I P M L K A N
G R O L M T I A K Z E
M U S E U M L S B H P
```

Wordsmart: Etymology

Narcissus, the handsome young man whom Echo loved, also contributed to English vocabulary. According to Greek mythology, Narcissus was so handsome that he fell in love with his own reflection in a pool of water and drowned while trying to reach it. From that tale comes *narcissist,* someone who is vain and self-absorbed; *narcissistic*, an adjective applied to such a person; and *narcissus,* the name of an attractive flower that often grows near water.

LESSON 26 Words Used in Sports

Target Words
aerobic, *adj.* referring to any exercise that conditions the lungs and heart
agile, *adj.* able to move quickly and easily
amateur, *n., adj.* a person who plays a sport for pleasure rather than for money; not professional
decathlon, *n.* an athletic contest that tests skills in ten events, including running, jumping, and throwing
equestrian, *n., adj.* one who rides a horse; relating to horseback riding
freestyle, *n., adj.* a race in which swimmers may use any stroke; referring to such a race
forfeit, *v., n.* to lose or give up; something surrendered as a penalty
league, *n.* an association of teams or clubs that compete among themselves
marathon, *n.* a footrace of 26 miles, 385 yards; a contest of endurance
triathlon, *n.* an athletic contest involving three consecutive events, usually swimming, bicycling, and running
tournament, *n.* a series of contests in a particular sport to determine a champion
varsity, *n.* a school's main team in any given sport

GETTING STARTED

The specialized vocabulary that people use in talking about sports might be unfamiliar to you. Context clues, comparisons, and restatements can help you understand these words.

I. Practice the Words

EXERCISE 1: Solve a Paragraph Puzzle

Use eight target words and your knowledge of context clues such as definition to fill in the blank spaces in this paragraph. Use each word only once, and be sure the words fit grammatically into the sentences.

agile	amateur	decathlon	equestrian
freestyle	marathon	triathlon	tournament

Rex is an _____ athlete with a body that moves quickly and easily. When he swims

in _____ races, events in which participants can use any stroke, he does the butterfly

stroke. He was once in a city _____, completing the nearly 27-mile run in good

time. In fact, if he improves his cycling, Rex could qualify for the Olympic _____,

which includes swimming, cycling, and running. His sister is an _____ who

competes in a series of events at a yearly horseback-riding _____. Rex's brother is a

discus thrower and hopes to be in the Olympic _____, a contest that consists of ten

events. Rex and his siblings are _____ athletes who do not get paid to play.

EXERCISE 2: Apply Meaning to Context

Select the best answer to each question about the boldfaced target words. Write the letter of the answer on the line before the question.

_____ **1.** Of these choices, which is the best **aerobic** exercise?

    a. curling your toes   **c.** climbing stairs

    b. twisting your head   **d.** stretching your arms

_____ **2.** Who plays on a school's **varsity** team?

    a. the best players   **c.** the weakest players

    b. the beginners   **d.** the most popular players

_____ **3.** Which of these actions shows that someone is **agile**?

    a. shoving an opponent   **c.** standing still for a long time

    b. doing a backward flip   **d.** memorizing a poem

_____ **4.** What would you see at a typical **tournament?**

    a. one long contest   **c.** contests in ten sports

    b. contests in three sports   **d.** a series of contests in one sport

_____ **5.** What distinguishes an **amateur** athlete from a professional?

    a. An amateur is self-taught.   **c.** An amateur is not paid.

    b. An amateur has no training.   **d.** An amateur is not competitive.

_____ **6.** What kind of stroke do swimmers use in the **freestyle?**

    a. butterfly stroke only   **c.** backstroke only

    b. crawl only   **d.** a stroke of their choice

_____ **7.** How many contests are there in a **decathlon?**

    a. three   **c.** a varying number

    b. ten   **d.** any multiple of ten

_____ **8.** Which of these is characteristic of a **marathon?**

    a. It involves a set distance.   **c.** It takes less than an hour

    b. It is performed in teams.   **d.** Participants wear helmets.

_____ **9.** Which items are part of the typical gear of an **equestrian** performance?

    a. jumprope and boxing gloves   **c.** javelin and discus

    b. high bar and parallel bar   **d.** boots and saddle

_____ **10.** Against whom do members of a **league** usually play?

    a. teams in their own league   **c.** teams not in any league

    b. teams in another league   **d.** individual members, not teams

EXERCISE 3: Use Target Words in Writing

On a separate sheet of paper, write a sentence about sports for each of the target words listed at the beginning of this lesson. Be sure your sentences show that you know what the words mean.

EXAMPLE agile   *The agile gymnast could do a cartwheel on a balance beam.*

EXERCISE 4: Determine True/False

On the line before each statement, write *T* if the statement is true. Write *F* if it is false. Use your knowledge of the boldfaced target words to help you decide

_____ **1.** An **aerobic** exercise helps improve your breathing.

_____ **2.** A **triathlon** is a **league** of three teams.

_____ **3.** The distance run in a **marathon** is shorter than the distance of most track races.

_____ **4.** A **tournament** always includes a pole vault.

_____ **5.** A school's best soccer players would usually be on its **varsity** team.

_____ **6.** An **equestrian** usually competes on horseback.

_____ **7.** A good swimmer might compete in both a **freestyle** and a **decathlon.**

_____ **8.** Athletes who practice hard often **forfeit** games.

_____ **9.** An **amateur** athlete is sometimes paid more than a corporate executive.

_____ **10.** A good speed skater must be **agile** as well as fast.

EXERCISE 5: Synonyms

On the line before each item, write the letter of the choice that is closest in meaning to the boldfaced target word.

_____ **1. agile**   **a.** stiff   **b.** carefree   **c.** flexible   **d.** exhausted

_____ **2. amateur**   **a.** talented   **b.** muscular   **c.** impractical **d.** unpaid

_____ **3. league**   **a.** team   **b.** association **c.** field   **d.** scorecard

_____ **4. forfeit**   **a.** surrender **b.** exchange   **c.** triumph   **d.** defeat

_____ **5. tournament** **a.** travel   **b.** victory   **c.** activity   **d.** championship

_____ **6. equestrian** **a.** swimmer   **b.** runner   **c.** rider   **d.** cyclist

_____ **7. triathlon**   **a.** contest   **b.** muscle   **c.** pole   **d.** oar

_____ **8. freestyle**   **a.** uniform   **b.** race   **c.** open-ended   **d.** smooth

UNIT 7

II. Vocabulary Challenge

EXERCISE 6: Speaking

Share what you know about the types of events that are held at the summer Olympic games or the athletes who participate in the contests. Use at least three target words in your discussion.

EXERCISE 7: Extend Your Vocabulary

Write the correct sport on the line after each clue. On the next line write three words that are related to that sport. An example has been done for you.

EXAMPLE   A word applied to athletes who can move quickly and easily.   *agile*
Related words: *flexible, graceful, fast*

1. This kind of athlete uses a saddle. _____

   Related words: _____

2. This competition is over 26 miles long. _____

   Related words: _____

3. This competition includes a Greek root meaning "ten." _____

   Related words: _____

4. This kind of activity is good for your heart and lungs. _____

   Related words: _____

5. In this competition, swimmers choose which strokes to use. _____

   Related words: _____

6. This contest involves three consecutive events. _____

   Related words: _____

Wordsmart: Etymology

The word *marathon* comes from a battle that took place in 490 B.C. near the Greek village of Marathon. After the Athenians defeated the Persians, a Greek runner was sent back to Athens to inform people of the great victory. His legendary long-distance run was later duplicated by other runners and became part of the Olympic games, which originated in ancient Greece. Today, marathons are held as annual events in many cities.

LESSON 27 Words from Long Ago

Target Words	Current Meaning	Original Meaning
beware, *v.*	to be on one's guard; to be cautious	*be-,* "be" + *war,* "watchful"
burden, *n., v.*	something heavy to carry or hard to bear; to weigh down	*byrthen,* "load"
forbid, *v.*	to prohibit; to rule out	*for-,* "away; off," + *beodan,* "ask; order"
knight, *n.*	a military servant to a king or lord	*cniht,* "boy; male retainer"
maiden, *n.*	an unmarried female	*mægden,* "young girl"
shrewd, *adj.*	sharply intelligent in a practical way	*screawa,* "shrew (small animal)"
tower, *n.*	a tall, slender structure or part of a building, often used to keep watch	*torr,* "tower"
wander, *v.*	to travel aimlessly about; to roam	*wandrian,* "wander"
wilderness, *n.*	an unsettled or untamed area	*wilde,* "wild," + *deor,* "wild animal, " + *-nes,* "state or condition of"
wily, *adj.*	able to trick others; sly	*vel,* "trick; stratagem"
worrisome, *adj.*	causing to feel annoyed, troubled, or anxious	*wyrgan,* "strangle; annoy" + *-sum,* "like; characterized by"
wrath, *n.*	intense anger; an angry act	*wrath,* "angry"

GETTING STARTED

You can understand words better if you know their origins. The word *shrewd,* for example, comes from the Old English word for a *shrew*—a small insect-eating animal with a long pointed snout and a bite once thought to be poisonous. With this information, you get an idea that a *shrewd* person is clever in a sharp, but sometimes harmful, way.

I. Practice the Words

EXERCISE 1: Understand Word Origins

On the line next to each target word, write a definition that reflects the word's Old English origins.

wilderness: _____

wily: _____

worrisome: _____

EXERCISE 2: Match Words and Origins

Match the word on the left with its origin on the right by writing the letter of the origin on the line after the word. Use each origin only once.

1. forbid ____   **a.** from the Old English for "young girl"

2. worrisome ____   **b.** from the Old English for "small animal"

3. knight ____   **c.** from the Old English for "trick"

4. maiden ____   **d.** from the Old English for "tower"

5. burden ____   **e.** from the Old English for "angry"

6. wily ____   **f.** from the Old English for "like strangling"

7. beware ____   **g.** from the Old English for "load"

8. wrath ____   **h.** from the Old English for "boy" or "retainer"

9. shrewd ____   **i.** from the Old English for "order off"

10. tower ____   **j.** from the Old English for "be watchful"

EXERCISE 3: Use Words in Context

Using the target words and your knowledge of sentence clues, fill in all the blank spaces in the paragraph. Use each word only once. Be sure the words fit grammatically into the sentences.

| beware | burden | forbid | knight | maiden | shrewd |
| tower | wander | wilderness | wily | worrisome | wrath |

Once there was a beautiful young _____ named Elinor who claimed to know

magic. In reality, she was a _____ person who used clever tricks to cheat

people out of their money. To put an end to her mischief, the king passed a law to

_____ the practice of magic, but Elinor ignored his ban. The king was known

far and wide for his fiery temper. Sir Lionel, a _____ who had fought for the

king, warned Elinor to _____ of the king's _____. "He will imprison you

in a high _____ at the top of a castle in the untamed _____ where wild

animals _____ aimlessly day and night. Even a _____ person like you, who

has a practical solution to every problem, will find it impossible to escape. I will

have the heavy _____ of rescuing you. It is a most _____ situation."

EXERCISE 4: Identify Synonyms and Antonyms

In each item below, a boldfaced target word is paired with another word. On the line before each pair, write *S* if the two words are synonyms. Write *A* if they are antonyms.

_____ 1. **shrewd**/impractical

_____ 2. **wrath**/fury

_____ 3. **maiden**/lad

_____ 4. **wilderness**/civilization

_____ 5. **wander**/roam

_____ 6. **burden**/weight

_____ 7. **forbid**/allow

_____ 8. **wily**/cunning

_____ 9. **worrisome**/troubling

_____ 10. **tower**/basement

EXERCISE 5: Apply Meanings to Context

Use what you know about the meanings and origins of the boldfaced target words to answer these questions. Write the letter of the best answer on the line before the question.

_____ 1. Which action best shows a teacher's **wrath?**
- **a.** punishing the class
- **b.** handing out a high grade
- **c.** organizing a class trip
- **d.** asking the class to study harder

_____ 2. What do parents often **forbid** their children to do?
- **a.** talk to strangers
- **b.** be polite
- **c.** finish their homework
- **d.** catch the school bus

_____ 3. When would be an appropriate time to yell **"Beware!"?**
- **a.** when proposing a toast
- **b.** when you win a prize
- **c.** when you are confused
- **d.** when there is danger

_____ 4. What does it mean when a camel is called a beast of **burden?**
- **a.** It travels in the desert.
- **b.** It can carry a heavy load.
- **c.** It has one or two humps.
- **d.** It is a wild animal.

_____ 5. What do you usually find in a church **tower?**
- **a.** people
- **b.** benches
- **c.** graves
- **d.** bells

_____ 6. What kind of character is a wandering **knight?**
- **a.** a nobleman who has no home
- **b.** a warrior for the king who travels
- **c.** a long-distance advisor to the king
- **d.** a restless enemy of the king

_____ 7. Which of these adjectives best describes a **maiden?**
- **a.** young and male
- **b.** old and male
- **c.** young and female
- **d.** old and married

_____ 8. Which event could be **worrisome?**
- **a.** winning an award
- **b.** planting a garden
- **c.** building a snow fort
- **d.** a hurricane forecast

II. Vocabulary Challenge

EXERCISE 6: Use Target Words in Writing

On a separate sheet of paper, write a paragraph that tells a tale about a knight in the Middle Ages. Use at least three target words in your paragraph.

EXERCISE 7: Extend Your Vocabulary

Match the word on the left with its meaning on the right by writing the letter of the meaning on the line after the word. Use your knowledge of the target words and their origins to help you. You can check your answers in a dictionary.

1. bewilder	_____	**a.**	an old word for a female servant
2. bidden	_____	**b.**	cautious
3. burdensome	_____	**c.**	a strong urge to travel
4. forbidden	_____	**d.**	sharp-tempered; often scolding others
5. handmaiden	_____	**e.**	a trick intended to deceive others; trickery
6. knighthood	_____	**f.**	to cause to be confused; to puzzle
7. shrewish	_____	**g.**	heavy; hard to bear
8. wanderlust	_____	**h.**	asked to appear or do something; summoned
9. wary	_____	**i.**	the rank or profession of a knight
10. wile	_____	**j.**	not allowed; banned

> **Wordsmart: Spelling**
>
> *Knight* is one of many words spelled with a silent *k* that come from Old English. The *k* sound in these words (which were spelled with a *c* in Old English) was once pronounced. Other words with a silent *k* before *n* that come from Old English include *knee, kneel, knife, knit, knock, knot,* and *know.*

LESSON 28 Words About Money

Target Words
accumulate, *v.* to gather; to grow into a large heap
bankrupt, *adj.* financially ruined; impoverished
debtor, *n.* a person who owes something to another
deposit, *v., n.* to give over for safekeeping; something, such as money, that is entrusted for safekeeping
generous, *adj.* willing to give or share; referring to a large amount
interest, *n.* money paid for the use of money, usually expressed as a percentage
invest, *v.* to use money in order to make a profit
poverty, *n.* lack of money; the state of being poor
thrifty, *adj.* very careful in the use of money; inclined to save money
wage, *n.* money paid for work
wealthy, *adj.* rich; having an abundance of material possessions
withdraw, *v.* to take money or something else out of a place where it is kept

GETTING STARTED

Whether you are buying lunch at school, solving a math problem, or opening a bank account, money is part of everyday life. In this lesson, you will learn words that will help you understand the language of money and write or discuss financial issues.

I. Practice the Words

EXERCISE 1: Solve a Paragraph Puzzle

Using the target words, fill in all the blank spaces in the paragraph. Use each word only once. Be sure the words fit grammatically into the sentences.

Renee is neither poor nor _____. She comes from a middle-class family.

From the _____ she earns on her part-time job at the bakery, she makes a

weekly _____ in the bank. A _____ person, she saves as much as she can

and tries not to _____ money from the bank unless she really needs it. Instead,

she lets it _____ in her account, where it earns a good rate of _____. She

hopes to save enough money to _____ in the stock of a company that will turn

a large profit. Renee's sister, Paula, on the other hand, loves to spend money. As a

result, she is a _____, with stacks of bills to pay. She was desperate when the

company she worked for could not pay its bills and went _____. She would

have faced months of hardship and _____ if Renee had not been _____

and given Paula the money she needed.

EXERCISE 2: Match Ideas to Context

Using your knowledge of the boldfaced target words, choose the answer that best completes each statement. Write the letter of your choice on the line in the statement.

1. When friends did not repay the money he lent them, Mr. Harding became _____ .
   a. wealthy   **b.** thrifty   **c.** bankrupt   **d.** generous

2. If you _____ your money wisely, it will earn more money for you.
   a. withdraw   **b.** deposit   **c.** invest   **d.** accumulate

3. You could see the signs of _____ in the run-down houses and the hungry-looking children.
   a. debtor   **b.** poverty   **c.** interest   **d.** wage

4. If you need money for the trip, you could _____ some of your savings from the bank.
   a. withdraw   **b.** invest   **c.** deposit   **d.** accumulate

5. Ken earned a higher hourly _____ after he asked his boss for a raise.
   a. deposit   **b.** interest   **c.** poverty   **d.** wage

6. The _____ avoided the lender because he owed him a hundred dollars.
   a. debtor   **b.** wage   **c.** poverty   **d.** deposit

7. Caleb was a _____ boy who shared his small allowance with his friends.
   a. wealthy   **b.** generous   **c.** bankrupt   **d.** thrifty

8. The _____ on his bank loan was 5 percent a year.
   a. deposit   **b.** wage   **c.** debtor   **d.** interest

EXERCISE 3: Identify Antonyms

On the line before each item, write the letter of the word that is most nearly the opposite of the boldfaced target word.

_____ **1. deposit**   **a.** remove   **b.** reply   **c.** whisper   **d.** depart

_____ **2. thrifty**   **a.** caring   **b.** expensive   **c.** cheap   **d.** wasteful

_____ **3. poverty**   **a.** greed   **b.** scarcity   **c.** riches   **d.** influence

_____ **4. debtor**   **a.** employee   **b.** lender   **c.** beggar   **d.** interviewer

_____ **5. generous**   **a.** broke   **b.** unhappy   **c.** stingy   **d.** kind

_____ **6. wealthy**   **a.** sore   **b.** poor   **c.** lowborn   **d.** elegant

_____ **7. accumulate**   **a.** distribute   **b.** arrange   **c.** emphasize   **d.** announce

_____ **8. bankrupt**   **a.** torn   **b.** slanted   **c.** selfish   **d.** enriched

UNIT 7

EXERCISE 4: Use Synonyms

On the line after each sentence, write the target word with the meaning closest to the boldfaced word in the sentence. Use each target word only once.

1. Clarence left his money in the bank so that it would **collect** interest.   _____

2. What **salary** does the job pay?   _____

3. Charleen is a **frugal** person who spends her money wisely.   _____

4. Tanya had to **remove** five hundred dollars from her bank account.   _____

5. When the Joneses went **broke,** they had to sell their home.   _____

6. The **rich** tycoon had a garage filled with antique cars.   _____

7. Mr. Kaplan is an **unselfish** person who often donates to charity.   _____

8. Ashamed of her **poorness,** Sonya pretended to have money.   _____

EXERCISE 5: Determine True/False

Each of the following statements contains at least one boldfaced target word. On the line before the statement, write *T* if it is true. Write *F* if it is false.

_____ 1. When you **deposit** money in a bank account, you are closing the account.

_____ 2. If you leave your money in a savings account, it will **accumulate interest.**

_____ 3. Some people **invest** in stocks and bonds.

_____ 4. A **debtor** may go **bankrupt** if he or she owes too much money.

_____ 5. When you **withdraw** money from your bank account, you are collecting a **wage.**

_____ 6. A **thrifty** person spends a lot of money on items he or she does not really need.

_____ 7. Going **bankrupt** usually makes a person **wealthy.**

_____ 8. A person in **poverty** can afford to be **generous.**

EXERCISE 6: Use Target Words in Writing

On a blank sheet of paper, write a sentence about earning or spending money for each of the target words listed at the beginning of this lesson. Be sure your sentences show that you know what the words mean.

EXAMPLE   interest   *When my parents borrowed money for our new house, the bank charged them 5 percent interest on the loan.*

II. Vocabulary Challenge

EXERCISE 7: Speaking

With a partner, role-play a visit to a bank. One of you take the role of a customer, and the other the role of a bank employee. Use at least four target words in your discussion.

EXERCISE 8: Word Play

Use the clues to fill in this crossword with the target words.

Across

4. Money paid on a loan
7. Pile up
8. Careful with money
10. Someone who owes
11. Take out
12. Not poor

Down

1. Unselfish
2. Financially ruined
3. A poor state
   of affairs
5. Money earned on
   the job
6. An antonym for remove
9. To put money in the
   stock market

Wordsmart: Etymology

Bankrupt contains the Latin root *rupt*, meaning "break" or "broken." To be *bankrupt* is "to have your bank broken, or be unable to pay your debts." Other words with the same root include *abrupt*, "broken off"; *disrupt*, "to break apart; to disturb"; *erupt*, "to break out"; *interrupt*, "to break into"; and *rupture*, "a break; to break."

Check Your Knowledge: Unit 7

By now you have added 48 new words to your vocabulary. Test your ability to use these words in the following exercises.

A. Determine Meaning from Context

On the line before each sentence, write the letter of the word or phrase that is closest in meaning to the boldfaced target word. Use the context clues to help you decide.

_____ **1.** The **debtor** owes money to two different banks.
    a. someone who lends money   **c.** someone who starts a business
    b. someone who borrows money   **d.** someone who loses a business

_____ **2.** Pam is a **thrifty** person who never spends on things she does not need.
    a. careful with money   **c.** not practical
    b. very poor   **d.** wasteful

_____ **3.** I gulped down two glasses of the delicious apricot **nectar.**
    a. a bitter medicine   **c.** a cup of milk
    b. a tasty beverage   **d.** a piece of fruit

_____ **4.** The storm was **furious,** with loud thunder and lightning.
    a. wild and angry   **c.** hot and humid
    b. playful and exciting   **d.** cool and refreshing

_____ **5.** I looked in the **atlas** to find the route from Chicago to New York.
    a. book of maps   **c.** newspaper ads
    b. book of poems   **d.** textbook

_____ **6.** Make a small **deposit** every week and watch your bank account grow.
    a. money owed to a bank   **c.** money borrowed from a bank
    b. money put into a bank   **d.** money removed from a bank

_____ **7.** Dodi never experienced **poverty** until her parents lost their jobs.
    a. the state of being lonely   **c.** the state of being an orphan
    b. the state of being angry   **d.** the state of being poor

_____ **8.** Because she is so **agile,** Bridget can do a backward double flip.
    a. delicate   **c.** able to move easily
    b. competitive   **d.** well trained

UNIT 7

B. Identify Synonyms

On the line before each item, write the letter of the word that is closest in meaning to the boldfaced target word.

_____ **1. wrath**   **a.** anger   **b.** creativity   **c.** sweetness   **d.** apology

_____ **2. fortune**   **a.** size   **b.** chance   **c.** confusion   **d.** helpfulness

_____ **3. wander**   **a.** respond   **b.** excel   **c.** rove   **d.** hurry

_____ **4. burden**   **a.** relief   **b.** strength   **c.** load   **d.** ease

_____ **5. wily**   **a.** untamed   **b.** dull   **c.** scholarly   **d.** tricky

_____ **6. forbid**   **a.** weaken   **b.** insult   **c.** ban   **d.** permit

_____ **7. odyssey**   **a.** story   **b.** voyage   **c.** warfare   **d.** courage

_____ **8. withdraw**   **a.** force   **b.** insert   **c.** remove   **d.** repair

C. Identify Antonyms

On the line before each item, write the letter of the word that is most nearly the opposite of the boldfaced target word.

_____ **1. amateur**   **a.** unpaid   **b.** devoted   **c.** professional   **d.** talented

_____ **2. worrisome**   **a.** painful   **b.** comforting   **c.** soft   **d.** loose

_____ **3. generous**   **a.** huge   **b.** excessive   **c.** sensitive   **d.** skimpy

_____ **4. panic**   **a.** hunger   **b.** peacefulness **c.** confusion   **d.** loudness

_____ **5. agile**   **a.** strong   **b.** graceful   **c.** clumsy   **d.** hasty

_____ **6. wealthy**   **a.** inferior   **b.** minor   **c.** defeated   **d.** penniless

_____ **7. shrewd**   **a.** foolish   **b.** careful   **c.** harsh   **d.** lenient

_____ **8. titanic**   **a.** puny   **b.** moody   **c.** blunt   **d.** awful

D. Use Words in Context

Choose the target word below that best completes each sentence, and write it on the line provided. Use each target word only once. Not all the listed target words will be used.

amateur	forfeit	interest	invest
museum	tournament	tower	wage

1. If the team is short a player, the rules say the team will have to _____ the game.

2. The bank pays me 5 percent _____ for allowing it to use my money.

3. The _____ had an exhibit of ancient Egyptian relics.

4. Shall I save my money in a bank or _____ it in stocks and bonds?

5. The bell _____ at the top of the church could be seen from miles away.

6. At the _____, several fine archers competed in a series of archery contests.

E. Determine True/False

On the line before each statement, write *T* if the statement is true. Write *F* if it is false. Use your knowledge of the boldfaced target words to help you decide.

_____ **1.** The teams in a **league** usually play against one another.

_____ **2.** There are nine events in a **triathlon.**

_____ **3.** A **knight** doing battle on horseback must have some **equestrian** skills.

_____ **4.** Discus throwing is one of the ten events in a **decathlon.**

_____ **5.** If you **deposit** money in a savings account, **interest** will **accumulate.**

_____ **6.** Someone on an **odyssey** might **wander** a long distance.

F. Identify Word Origins

Match the target words and their origins by writing the letter of the origin on the line after the target word. Use your understanding of the target word's meaning to help you decide. Use each origin only once.

1. amazon _____   **a.** from Roman mythology, the goddess of agriculture

2. Olympian _____   **b.** from the Old English for "young woman"

3. beware _____   **c.** from Greek mythology, a nymph who was disappointed in love

4. cereal _____   **d.** from the Old English for "boy" or "male retainer"

5. echo _____   **e.** from Greek mythology, a female warrior

6. knight _____   **f.** from the Old English for "be watchful"

7. maiden _____   **g.** from Greek mythology, a mountain where the gods supposedly lived

G. Match Ideas

On the line before each item, write the letter of the target word from the list below that is most clearly related to the situation described in the sentence. Use each word only once.

aerobic   bankrupt   freestyle   marathon
panic   varsity   wilderness

_____ **1.** The swimmer can choose whichever stroke she prefers.

_____ **2.** Jumping up and down conditions the lungs and heart.

_____ **3.** The scream sent the people running madly to the doors.

_____ **4.** Joel belongs to the school's best basketball team.

_____ **5.** The company can no longer pay its debts.

_____ **6.** The jungle has never been tamed, and few human beings go there.

_____ **7.** A runner trains to run over 26 miles.

Spelling

LESSON 1 TEACHING
Silent *e* words and suffixes

require	→ requiring	requires	requirement
achieve	→ achieving	achieves	achievement
provide	→ providing	provides	
separate	→ separating	separates	separately
pursue	→ pursuing	pursues	
complete	→ completing	completes	completely
imagine	→ imagining	imagines	
introduce	→ introducing	introduces	
continue	→ continuing	continues	

LESSON GENERALIZATION: A **suffix** is a word ending that changes the use of a word. To add a suffix to a word that ends with a final silent **e**, drop the **e** if the suffix begins with a vowel. Keep the **e** if the suffix begins with a consonant.

pursuing   completely

A. Complete the following exercise.

1. When **ing** is added to words ending in a silent **e,** what happens to the e?

_____

Write those words ending in **ing**.

_____   _____   _____

_____   _____   _____

2. When **s, ment,** and **ly** are added to the words ending in silent **e,** what happens to the e?

_____

Write the words ending in **s, ment,** and **ly.**

_____   _____   _____

_____   _____   _____

_____   _____   _____

_____

B. On a separate sheet of paper, use each word with a suffix in an original sentence.

SPELLING

1 Silent *e* words and suffixes

1. requiring
2. requires
3. requirement
4. achieving
5. achieves
6. achievement
7. providing
8. provides

9. separating
10. separates
11. separately
12. pursuing
13. pursues
14. completing
15. completes
16. completely

17. imagining
18. imagines
19. introducing
20. introduces
21. continuing
22. continues

A. Complete each pair of sentences with two forms of the underlined word.

1. **separate**   Let's wrap each gift _____.

    Miguel is _____ the puzzle into pieces.

2. **require**   Past experience is one _____ for the job.

    The coach will be _____ more practice time.

3. **pursue**   The police were _____ the speeding car.

    Our art teacher _____ her own art projects.

4. **complete**   Marcia never _____ her work early.

    The paint is not _____ dry yet.

5. **achieve**   Climbing that mountain would be a great _____.

    Mark _____ every goal he sets for himself.

6. **introduce**   Carol keeps _____ me to her friends.

    Walk on stage after the speaker _____ you.

7. **continue**   The program _____ after the intermission.

    The baby was _____ to cry.

8. **provide**   A local store is _____ uniforms for the team.

    That tree _____ us with apples every autumn.

9. **imagine**   My brother _____ he sees pictures in the clouds.

    I keep _____ I hear footsteps downstairs.

B. On a separate sheet of paper, write the **ing** form of the spelling words in alphabetical order. Then write the **s** form of each word.

LESSON
2 TEACHING
The suffix *ance*

clear + ance = clear<u>ance</u>	inherit + ance = inherit<u>ance</u>
perform + ance = perform<u>ance</u>	annoy + ance = annoy<u>ance</u>
disturb + ance = disturb<u>ance</u>	avoid + ance = avoid<u>ance</u>
allow + ance = allow<u>ance</u>	resemble + ance = resembl<u>ance</u>
accept + ance = accept<u>ance</u>	insure + ance = insur<u>ance</u>
attend + ance = attend<u>ance</u>	endure + ance = endur<u>ance</u>
assist + ance = assist<u>ance</u>	assure + ance = assur<u>ance</u>
appear + ance = appear<u>ance</u>	observe + ance = observ<u>ance</u>
acquaint + ance = acquaint<u>ance</u>	guide + ance = guid<u>ance</u>

LESSON GENERALIZATION: The suffix **ance** is commonly added to complete
words to form nouns or adjectives.

Her <u>resemblance</u> to her sister was amazing.

He made an <u>acceptance</u> speech.

A. Compete the following exercises.

1. Look for base words in the word list that end in silent **e.** When the suffix **ance** is added to

those words, what happens to the final **e** of each base word? _____

Write the spelling words that are created when **ance** is added to a base word with a final
silent **e.**

_____   _____   _____

_____   _____   _____

2. What happens when **ance** is added to a base word that does not end in a silent **e?**

_____

Write those spelling words that are created when **ance** is added to a base word that does
not end in a silent **e.**

_____   _____   _____

_____   _____   _____

_____   _____   _____

B. On a separate sheet of paper, use each spelling word in a sentence. Then rewrite the sentences,
leaving a blank for the spelling words. Arrange your sentences in an order that does not match the order
the spelling words are presented in the list. Then trade papers with a partner and try to fill in the blanks.

SPELLING

2 The suffix *ance*

1. clearance
2. performance
3. allowance
4. disturbance
5. acceptance
6. attendance
7. assistance
8. appearance
9. acquaintance
10. inheritance
11. annoyance
12. avoidance
13. resemblance
14. insurance
15. endurance
16. assurance
17. observance
18. guidance

A. Complete each sentence with a word from the spelling list.

1. Mark spent his _____ to buy a football.

2. The actor gave a good _____ in tonight's play.

3. The department store had a _____ sale on summer clothing.

4. All of the concert's organizers expected _____ to be excellent.

5. The two workers needed _____ in moving the huge crate.

6. The dog created a _____ when it ran into the store.

7. Fraternal twins may show little _____ to each other.

8. The governor made a brief _____ at the state fair.

9. Is Myra a good friend or only an _____?

10. Race car drivers need good accident _____.

11. The newly elected class president prepared an _____ speech.

12. Long-distance swimming requires great _____.

13. The town's _____ of the Fourth of July included parades and fireworks.

14. Leon got everyone's _____ that they would be on time.

15. The will stated that each person was to receive an _____ of $1,000.

16. My aunt is a school _____ counselor.

17. The loud noise brought a look of _____ to the librarian's face.

18. Some diets require the _____ of certain foods.

B. On a separate sheet of paper, create a word search puzzle using all of the words from the spelling list. Trade puzzles with a partner. Try to solve your partner's puzzle. Can you find all 18 words?.

LESSON
3 **TEACHING**

Plurals of words that end with *o*

studio + s	= studio<u>s</u>	banjo + s	= banjo<u>s</u>
radio + s	= radio<u>s</u>	piano + s	= piano<u>s</u>
rodeo + s	= rodeo<u>s</u>	kangaroo + s	= kangaroo<u>s</u>
stereo + s	= stereo<u>s</u>	zero + s	= zero<u>s</u>
patio + s	= patio<u>s</u>	lasso + s	= lasso<u>s</u>
ratio + s	= ratio<u>s</u>	halo + s	= halo<u>s</u>
igloo + s	= igloo<u>s</u>	silo + s	= silo<u>s</u>

echo + es	= echo<u>es</u>	potato + es	= potato<u>es</u>
hero + es	= hero<u>es</u>	tomato + es	= tomato<u>es</u>

LESSON GENERALIZATION: Singular means one. **Plural** means more than one.
Most singular nouns are made plural by adding the letter **s.** Most nouns that end with
the letter **o** are also made plural by adding the letter **s.** A few nouns that end with **o**
are made plural by adding **es.**

A. Complete the following exercise.

1. Most singular nouns ending in **o** are made plural by adding _____.
Write the plural forms of the words from the word list that follow this rule.

_____   _____   _____

_____   _____   _____

_____   _____   _____

_____

2. A few nouns ending in **o** are an exception to the rule. These exceptions are made plural
by adding _____. Write the plural forms of the words from the word
list that are exceptions to the rule.

_____   _____   _____

_____

B. On a separate sheet of paper, write the plural forms of the words from the word
list in alphabetical order. Check your list to make sure that you have added the
correct plural endings.

LESSON
3 MORE PRACTICE

Plurals of words that end with *o*

SPELLING

1. studios	7. igloos	13. halos
2. radios	8. banjos	14. silos
3. rodeos	9. pianos	15. echoes
4. stereos	10. kangaroos	16. heroes
5. patios	11. zeros	17. potatoes
6. ratios	12. lassos	18. tomatoes

A. The words in each group are related in some way. Find words from the spelling list that fit into each group.

1. carrots, onions, _____ , _____

2. recorders, phonographs, _____ , _____

3. guitars, organs, _____ , _____

4. horses, cowboys, _____ , _____

5. huts, apartments, tepees, _____

6. decks, porches, terraces, _____

B. Write the plural form of the spelling word that matches each clue and fits in the puzzle.

Across

3. relation of one number to another

5. Australian animal

7. number

11. artist's work room

12. Western talent contest

Down

1. ring of light

2. ice house

4. paved area by a house

6. place to store grain

8. broadcasting device

9. repeated sound

10. record players

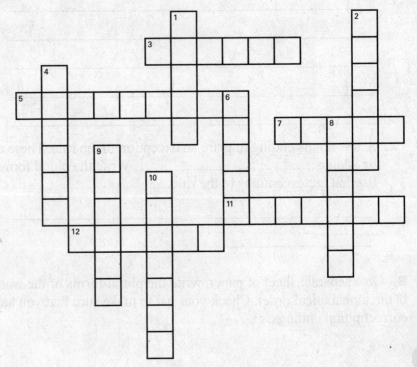

LESSON
4 TEACHING
Prefixes and base words

re + search	= <u>re</u>search	dis + courage	= <u>dis</u>courage	pre + caution	= <u>pre</u>caution
re + condition	= <u>re</u>condition	dis + prove	= <u>dis</u>prove	pre + arrange	= <u>pre</u>arrange
re + fuel	= <u>re</u>fuel	dis + ability	= <u>dis</u>ability	pre + diction	= <u>pre</u>diction
re + vision	= <u>re</u>vision	dis + agreement	= <u>dis</u>agreement	pre + mature	= <u>pre</u>mature
re + elect	= <u>re</u>elect	dis + advantage	= <u>dis</u>advantage	pre + face	= <u>pre</u>face
re + surface	= <u>re</u>surface	dis + regard	= <u>dis</u>regard	pre + school	= <u>pre</u>school

LESSON GENERALIZATION: A **prefix** is a group of letters added to the beginning of a word to make a word with a different meaning. A prefix can be added directly to a complete word to make a new word. No change is made in the prefix or the base word.

A. Complete the following exercises.

1. Look at the words in the list above. Note that when a prefix is added to each base word, neither the prefix nor the base word changes spelling. What prefix is added to the words in the first column?

   _____ Write those words. Circle the prefix in each.

   _____   _____   _____

   _____   _____   _____

2. What prefix is added to the words in the second column? _____
   Write those words. Circle the prefix in each.

   _____   _____   _____

   _____   _____   _____

3. What prefix is added to the words in the third column? _____
   Write those words. Circle the prefix in each.

   _____   _____   _____

   _____   _____   _____

B. Mix and match prefixes and base words using only the words in the list. Try new combinations until you find real words, and write the words on a separate sheet of paper. Compare your list to a partner's list.

Name _____   Date _____

1. research
2. recondition
3. refuel
4. revision
5. reelect
6. resurface
7. discourage
8. disprove
9. disability
10. disagreement
11. disadvantage
12. disregard
13. precaution
14. prearrange
15. prediction
16. premature
17. preface
18. preschool

A. Add the missing vowels to complete each spelling word.

1. d ____ s ____ dv ____ nt ____ g ____
2. pr ____ c ____ ____ t ____ ____ n
3. pr ____ ____ rr ____ ng ____
4. d ____ s ____ gr ____ ____ m ____ nt
5. d ____ sr ____ g ____ rd
6. pr ____ m ____ t ____ r ____

7. d ____ s ____ b ____ l ____ ty
8. r ____ s ____ ____ rch
9. r ____ v ____ s ____ ____ n
10. r ____ f ____ ____ l
11. pr ____ f ____ c ____
12. r ____ s ____ rf ____ c ____

B. Complete each sentence with a word from the spelling list.

1. Did the two boys have a _____ over who would be in charge?

2. Did you _____ your absence with the attendance office beforehand?

3. Rina had read only the _____ of the book.

4. Mark was doing _____ on sharks for his report.

5. The counselors took every _____ to make the camp safe for children.

6. The drivers must _____ their cars twice during the race.

7. Will losing the contest _____ Fran from trying again?

8. The 4:00 A.M. announcement that school would close due to snow was _____.

9. Jim had been absent, so he was at a _____ when he took the test.

10. Will your little brother attend _____ this year?

11. Leon does not consider his injury to be a serious _____.

12. This polish helps to _____ old leather.

13. Do you think the class will _____ the same officers?

14. We all made a _____ about who would win the World Series.

15. The scientist was unable to _____ the excellent research.

LESSON 5 TEACHING
Prefixes and roots

in + sist = in<u>sist</u>	in + spire = in<u>spire</u>	in + struct = in<u>struct</u>
con + sist = con<u>sist</u>	con + spire = con<u>spire</u>	con + struct = con<u>struct</u>
in + clude = in<u>clude</u>	in + flict = in<u>flict</u>	de + tain = de<u>tain</u>
con + clude = con<u>clude</u>	con + flict = con<u>flict</u>	re + tain = re<u>tain</u>
in + flate = in<u>flate</u>	de + cline = de<u>cline</u>	in + cis + ion = in<u>cision</u>
de + flate = de<u>flate</u>	re + cline = re<u>cline</u>	de + cis + ion = de<u>cision</u>

LESSON GENERALIZATION: Most **roots** are word parts that cannot stand alone. They become words when they are joined to prefixes (added before roots) or suffixes (added after roots). A root can be joined with many different prefixes. Changing the prefix changes the meaning.

in (in, into) + **struct** (build) = **instruct**   <u>instruct</u> people
con (together, with) + **struct** (build) = **construct**   <u>construct</u> buildings

A. Complete the following exercises.

1. What four prefixes are added to the roots in the word list?

_____   _____

_____   _____

2. Nine roots are used in the words from the word list. Write each root and the two prefixes that have been added to that root.

Prefix	**Prefix**	**Root**
_____	_____	_____
_____	_____	_____
_____	_____	_____
_____	_____	_____
_____	_____	_____
_____	_____	_____
_____	_____	_____
_____	_____	_____
_____	_____	_____

B. On a separate sheet of paper, write the words from the spelling list with a brief definition for each.

LESSON 5 — MORE PRACTICE
Prefixes and roots

1. insist
2. consist
3. instruct
4. construct
5. inflict
6. conflict
7. detain
8. retain
9. decline
10. recline
11. inspire
12. conspire
13. include
14. conclude
15. incision
16. decision
17. inflate
18. deflate

A. Unscramble the letters and write the spelling word. First, find the letters of the prefix. They are not scrambled.

1. tsinis _____
2. antrei _____
3. riconpes _____
4. elccondu _____
5. siinnoic _____
6. iclintf _____
7. rstcuint _____
8. tlconcfi _____
9. feldeat _____
10. siidenco _____
11. atdeni _____
12. stconsi _____
13. ledincu _____
14. creilne _____
15. tsurccont _____
16. prinesi _____
17. nildece _____
18. talfine _____

B. Write the word from the spelling list that is the synonym (means the same) or antonym (means the opposite) of each word below.

1. scheme (synonym) _____
2. begin (antonym) _____
3. cut (synonym) _____
4. demand (synonym) _____
5. destroy (antonym) _____
6. stand (antonym) _____
7. accord (synonym) _____
8. shrink (antonym) _____
9. delay (synonym) _____
10. teach (synonym) _____
11. discourage (antonym) _____
12. remember (synonym) _____
13. judgment (synonym) _____
14. inflate (antonym) _____
15. refuse (synonym) _____
16. impose (synonym) _____
17. peace (antonym) _____
18. omit (antonym) _____

LESSON
6 TEACHING
Words ending with *ary*

tempor**ary**	compliment**ary**	diet**ary**
summ**ary**	extraordin**ary**	heredit**ary**
liter**ary**	honor**ary**	supplement**ary**
second**ary**	volunt**ary**	burgl**ary**
prim**ary**	contempor**ary**	itiner**ary**
prelimin**ary**	solit**ary**	necess**ary**

LESSON GENERALIZATION: The **ary** ending begins with a vowel that is indistinct. The **a** is difficult to tell from an **e** when it is followed by the letter **r**. The ending **ary** can sound almost like **ery** in **very**. Remember that the ending **ary** is more common than **ery**.

A. Complete the following exercises.

1. What ending is added to each word in the word list? _____

2. Although the endings **ary** and **ery** sound very much alike, one ending is far less common than the other. That ending is _____. Write the words from the word list that end in **ary**.

_____ _____ _____

_____ _____ _____

_____ _____ _____

_____ _____ _____

_____ _____ _____

_____ _____ _____

B. On a separate sheet of paper, make a word search puzzle using all 18 spelling words. Trade puzzles with a partner. Try to solve your partner's puzzle. Make a list of all the words you are able to find. How well can you do?

SPELLING

6 Words ending with *ary*

1. temporary
2. summary
3. literary
4. secondary
5. primary
6. preliminary
7. complimentary
8. extraordinary
9. honorary
10. voluntary
11. contemporary
12. solitary
13. dietary
14. hereditary
15. supplementary
16. burglary
17. itinerary
18. necessary

A. Write the words from the spelling list that match the clues and fit the boxes. Circle the hidden word your answers reveal.

1. high school level

2. done by choice

3. before the main event

4. the first in order; basic

5. having to do with books

6. only one

7. lasting only a short time

8. passed through generations

9. having to do with respect

10. existing at the same time

11. a brief report

12. very unusual

13. having to do with food

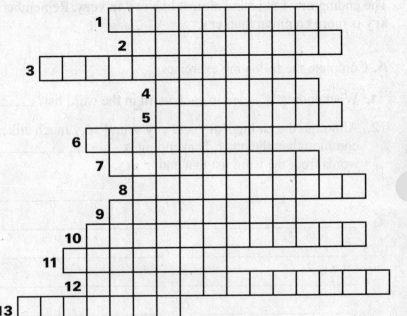

B. Rearrange the groups of words to make complete sentences. Use correct capitalization and punctuation. Underline the words from the spelling list.

1. necessary be a complete may itinerary not

_____

2. complimentary a received ticket show everyone to the extraordinary

_____

3. the preliminary steps captain took to passengers from burglary safeguard

_____

4. vitamins program in this supplementary included are dietary

_____

LESSON
7 TEACHING
Soft and hard *g*

ener**g**y	ea**g**le
re**g**ister	re**g**ulation
le**g**end	le**g**al
a**g**ent	ar**g**ument
ori**g**in	or**g**anize
obli**g**e	obli**g**ation
alle**g**iance	alli**g**ator
genius	**gu**itar
re**g**ion	reco**g**nize

LESSON GENERALIZATION: When the letter **g** has a soft sound (ginger, gym), it is usually followed by the letter **i, e,** or **y.** When the letter **g** has a hard sound (game, magnet), it is often followed by a consonant or by the vowel **a, o,** or **u.**

A. Complete the following exercises.

1. Read the words in the word list above. Listen for the soft **g** sound and the hard **g.** What letters follow the soft **g**?

_____   _____   _____

Write the words from the list that have a soft **g.**

_____   _____   _____

_____   _____   _____

_____   _____   _____

2. What vowels often follow a hard **g**?

_____   _____   _____

Write the words from the list that have a hard **g** sound.

_____   _____   _____

_____   _____   _____

_____   _____   _____

B. On a separate sheet of paper, write in alphabetical order the nine words that contain a soft **g** sound. Then write in alphabetical order the nine words from the word list that contain a hard **g** sound.

LESSON 7 MORE PRACTICE

Soft and hard *g*

SPELLING

1. energy	7. allegiance	13. argument
2. register	8. genius	14. organize
3. legend	9. region	15. obligation
4. agent	10. eagle	16. alligator
5. origin	11. regulation	17. guitar
6. oblige	12. legal	18. recognize

A. Use the definitions to find the soft **g** words that fit in the puzzle.

1. loyalty

2. do a favor for

3. a person who acts for another

4. power; force

5. an old story

6. extreme intelligence

7. a beginning

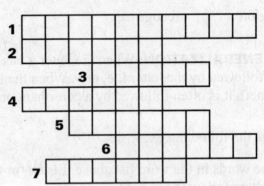

Use the definitions to find the hard **g** words that fit in the puzzle.

1. a rule or law

2. a stringed instrument

3. lawful

4. a large reptile

5. a disagreement

6. to arrange

7. a promise or duty

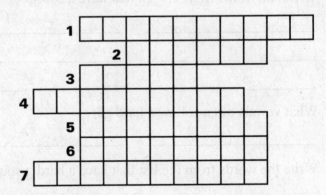

B. Find the misspelled word in each group. Write it correctly on the line.

1. oblige, argument, allegance

_____

2. regaster, alligator, origin

_____

3. genius, reckognize, energy

_____

4. agent, regin, obligation

_____

5. eagel, energy, genius

_____

6. argument, orginize, origin

_____

LESSON 8 Review

1. requirement
2. separating
3. continues
4. introducing
5. performance
6. acquaintance
7. observance

8. radios
9. zeros
10. potatoes
11. revision
12. reelect
13. disadvantage
14. prediction

15. construct
16. include
17. decision
18. summary
19. complimentary
20. voluntary

21. register
22. legend
23. argument
24. organize
25. energy

A. An analogy is a way of showing how words go together. Look at the first pair of words in each item. How are the words related? Write the spelling word that makes the second pair of words go together in the same way as the first pair.

1. organize is to **organizing** as **introduce** is to _____

2. legend is to **legendary** as **compliment** is to _____

3. achieve is to **achievement** as **require** is to _____

4. fuel is to **refuel** as **elect** is to _____

5. lasso is to **lassos** as **radio** is to _____

6. ability is to **disability** as **advantage** is to _____

7. assist is to **assistance** as **acquaint** is to _____

8. provide is to **providing** as **separate** is to _____

9. endure is to **endurance** as **observe** is to _____

10. imagine is to **imagines** as **continue** is to _____

B. Three words in each row follow the same spelling pattern. One word does not. Circle the word.

1. alligator guitar oblige obligation

2. ratios banjos silos declines

3. inspire inflict insist itinerary

4. dietary honorary disregard supplementary

5. consisting appearing constructing providing

6. origin legal genius imagine

7. decision discourage disprove disagreement

8. inspiring imagining insisting completing

9. acceptance annoyance inheritance disadvantage

SPELLING

LESSON 8 Review

energy	stereos	zeros
construct	legend	argument
prediction	voluntary	summary
include	revision	decision
allegiance	igloos	alligator
acquaintance	conclude	allowance
disagreement	kangaroo	

A. Match each word or phrase below to its synonym (S) or antonym (A) in the word list.

1. brief statement (S) _____

2. betrayal (A) _____

3. sluggishness (A) _____

4. story (S) _____

5. first draft (A) _____

6. sound systems (S) _____

7. forecast (S) _____

8. disagreement (S) _____

9. forced (A) _____

10. destroy (A) _____

11. choice (S) _____

12. exclude (A) _____

B. Complete each analogy using one of the words from the list.

1. **weak** is to **strong** as **agreement** is to _____

2. **worker** is to **pay** as **child** is to _____

3. **start** is to **begin** as **finish** is to _____

4. **grass** is to **huts** as **snow** is to _____

5. **trunk** is to **elephant** as **pouch** is to _____

6. **help** is to **assistance** as **loyalty** is to _____

7. **tree** is to **monkey** as **river** is to _____

8. **stories** is to **legends** as **numbers** is to _____

9. **sister** is to **relative** as **friend** is to _____

LESSON 9 TEACHING
Final *y* words and suffixes

betray	→ betrays	betrayed	betraying	attorney	→ attorneys
employ	→ employs	employed	employing	survey	→ surveys
portray	→ portrays	portrayed	portraying	ceremony	→ ceremonies
qualify	→ qualifies	qualified	qualifying	remedy	→ remedies
deny	→ denies	denied	denying		
occupy	→ occupies	occupied	occupying		

LESSON GENERALIZATION: When the letter before a final **y** is a vowel, the **y** does not change when a suffix is added. When the letter before a final **y** is a consonant, change the **y** to **i** before adding **es** or **ed.** Never change a final **y** to **i** when adding the suffix **ing.**

A. Complete the following exercises.

1. When a suffix is added to a word ending in a vowel-**y** combination, what happens to the **y**?
   _____ Write the words from the list that end in a vowel-**y** combination.

   _____   _____   _____

   _____   _____   _____

   _____   _____   _____

   _____   _____   _____

2. When a suffix other than **ing** is added to a word ending in a consonant-**y** combination, what

   happens to the **y**? _____ Write the words from the list that end in a
   consonant-**y** combination. (Do not include words with the **ing** suffix.)

   _____   _____   _____

   _____   _____   _____

   _____   _____

3. When **ing** is added to any word ending in **y**, what happens to the **y**? _____
   Write the words from the list that end in a **y-ing** combination.

   _____   _____   _____

   _____   _____   _____

B. On a separate sheet of paper, write a short story using at least ten words from the spelling list. Underline the spelling words in each sentence.

SPELLING

9 Final *y* words and suffixes

1. betrays	9. portraying	17. denying
2. betrayed	10. attorneys	18. occupies
3. betraying	11. surveys	19. occupied
4. employs	12. qualifies	20. occupying
5. employed	13. qualified	21. ceremonies
6. employing	14. qualifying	22. remedies
7. portrays	15. denies	
8. portrayed	16. denied	

A. Write the base form, the **ed** form, or the **ing** form of a spelling word that completes each sentence.

1. The _____ presented her client's case to the jury.

2. Carolyn could not find a _____ for her cold.

3. Robbie had not _____ to be on the wrestling team.

4. We took a _____ to determine the most popular song.

5. Jennifer received a trophy at the awards _____ held in the gym.

6. Seth _____ a mean character in the school play.

7. The theater will be _____ two more ushers.

8. The movie star had _____ the entire top floor of the hotel.

9. Tom felt that his friend had _____ him by telling the secret.

10. The request for tickets was _____ because it arrived too late.

B. Find and circle 12 words from the spelling list in the word search puzzle. Words appear forward, backward, up, and down.

D	E	Y	A	R	T	E	B	L	C	Y	F	R	A	T	B	F
F	P	O	R	T	R	A	Y	S	O	C	C	U	P	I	E	D
Q	T	G	R	E	M	E	D	I	E	S	T	A	G	G	T	H
Z	N	N	B	N	I	D	E	I	N	E	D	T	N	N	R	K
C	E	R	E	M	O	N	I	E	S	A	S	I	I	I	A	R
A	T	T	O	R	N	E	Y	S	W	V	Y	F	Y	Y	Y	O
M	G	N	I	Y	A	R	T	R	O	P	O	Y	O	N	I	F
Q	U	A	L	I	F	Y	I	N	G	N	L	I	L	E	N	D
R	I	D	S	Y	E	V	R	U	S	V	P	N	P	D	G	V

LESSON 10 TEACHING
The suffix *able*

tax + able = tax<u>able</u>	quote + able = quot<u>able</u>
remark + able = remark<u>able</u>	value + able = valu<u>able</u>
comfort + able = comfort<u>able</u>	imagine + able = imagin<u>able</u>
respect + able = respect<u>able</u>	note + able = not<u>able</u>
consider + able = consider<u>able</u>	advise + able = advis<u>able</u>
predict + able = predict<u>able</u>	rely + able = reli<u>able</u>
question + able = question<u>able</u>	vary + able = vari<u>able</u>
favor + able = favor<u>able</u>	envy + able = envi<u>able</u>
bear + able = bear<u>able</u>	
enjoy + able = enjoy<u>able</u>	

LESSON GENERALIZATION: The suffix **able,** meaning "able to be," is commonly added to complete words to form adjectives.

taxable = able to be taxed   **imaginable** = able to be imagined

If the base word ends with a silent **e,** drop the **e** before adding the suffix **able.**

If the base word ends with a consonant + **y,** change the **y** to **i** before adding **able.**

A. Complete the following exercises.

1. When the suffix **able** is added to a base word ending in a consonant or a vowel-**y** combination, do not change the spelling of the base word. Write the words from the word list that follow this spelling rule.

   _____   _____   _____

   _____   _____   _____

   _____   _____   _____

   _____

2. When the suffix **able** is added to a base word ending in a silent **e,** drop the **e.** Write the words from the list that follow this rule.

   _____   _____   _____

   _____   _____

3. When the suffix **able** is added to a base word ending in a consonant-**y** combination, change the **y** to **i.** Write the words from the list that follow this rule.

   _____   _____   _____

B. On a separate sheet of paper, write the words from the word list in alphabetical order.

SPELLING

10 The suffix *able*

1. taxable	7. questionable	13. imaginable
2. remarkable	8. favorable	14. notable
3. comfortable	9. bearable	15. advisable
4. respectable	10. enjoyable	16. reliable
5. considerable	11. quotable	17. variable
6. predictable	12. valuable	18. enviable

A. Add the **able** suffix to each base word.

1. predict _____

2. rely _____

3. comfort _____

4. consider _____

5. quote _____

6. vary _____

7. remark _____

8. enjoy _____

9. envy _____

10. value _____

11. tax _____

12. imagine _____

13. note _____

14. respect _____

15. favor _____

16. question _____

17. advise _____

18. bear _____

B. Answer each question with the **able** form of a word from the spelling list. The underlined words give a clue to the word you should use.

1. Must you <u>pay a tax</u> on the items you bought?

_____

2. Can you <u>depend on</u> that clock?

_____

3. Did you <u>enjoy</u> going to the play?

_____

4. Could you <u>predict</u> the outcome of the game?

_____

5. Was there <u>some doubt</u> about the field trip?

_____

LESSON 11 TEACHING
Words ending with *al* + *ly*

accidental + ly = accident**ally**   verbal + ly = verb**ally**
intentional + ly = intention**ally**   factual + ly = factu**ally**
occasional + ly = occasion**ally**   global + ly = glob**ally**
additional + ly = addition**ally**   physical + ly = physic**ally**
incidental + ly = incident**ally**   practical + ly = practic**ally**
national + ly = nation**ally**   typical + ly = typic**ally**
exceptional + ly = exception**ally**   oral + ly = or**ally**
general + ly = gener**ally**   partial + ly = parti**ally**
usual + ly = usu**ally**   vocal + ly = voc**ally**

LESSON GENERALIZATION: Add the suffix **ly** directly to adjectives ending with **al.**
Do not drop the **l** at the end of the base word. Do not drop the **l** in the **ly** suffix.

A. Complete the following exercises.

1. The words ending with **al** are all what part of speech? _____

2. What part of speech are the words ending in **ly**? _____

3. When you form an adverb by adding **ly** to an adjective ending in **al,** do not drop any letters.
   Write the adverbs from the word list.

_____   _____   _____

_____   _____   _____

_____   _____   _____

_____   _____   _____

_____   _____   _____

B. Using a dictionary or thesaurus, find synonyms that are also adverbs for each word in the
spelling list.

_____   _____   _____

_____   _____   _____

_____   _____   _____

_____   _____   _____

11 Words ending with *al* + *ly*

1. accidentally
2. intentionally
3. occasionally
4. additionally
5. incidentally
6. nationally
7. exceptionally
8. generally
9. usually
10. verbally
11. factually
12. globally
13. physically
14. practically
15. typically
16. orally
17. partially
18. vocally

A. Write the spelling word that matches the meaning of the underlined words in each sentence.

1. Therese did <u>not</u> drop the dish <u>on purpose</u>. _____

2. The President is known <u>throughout the nation</u>. _____

3. <u>In general</u>, the company fills its orders quickly. _____

4. <u>Sometimes</u> famous people visit here. _____

5. We are having a <u>characteristically</u> hectic day. _____

6. Tim's paper was only <u>halfway</u> finished. _____

7. The company set up offices <u>all over the world</u>. _____

8. <u>In addition</u>, Leo will need a snorkel and fins. _____

9. Did Mary put the papers on the table <u>on purpose</u>? _____

10. Bill spoke <u>with many facts</u> about the issues. _____

11. Mandy is <u>almost always</u> on time for the games. _____

12. <u>In physical stature</u>, Allen is larger than Jim. _____

13. Janet is an <u>unusually</u> good organist. _____

14. <u>By the way</u>, which book did you decide to buy? _____

15. The play was <u>almost</u> over when we arrived. _____

B. Unscramble the letters to make the adjective form of a spelling word.

1. clova _____
2. lidcctaena _____
3. realvb _____
4. neegalr _____
5. hicaypls _____
6. rictapcal _____
7. riltapa _____
8. tuacfal _____

LESSON
12 TEACHING
The prefix *com*

com + junction	= <u>con</u>junction	com + stant	= <u>con</u>stant
com + vention	= <u>con</u>vention	com + sent	= <u>con</u>sent
com + sider	= <u>con</u>sider	com + cert	= <u>con</u>cert
com + cern	= <u>con</u>cern	com + gress	= <u>con</u>gress
com + munication	= <u>com</u>munication	com + bination	= <u>com</u>bination
com + mittee	= <u>com</u>mittee	com + plicate	= <u>com</u>plicate
com + mend	= <u>com</u>mend	com + petition	= <u>com</u>petition
com + mence	= <u>com</u>mence	com + plaint	= <u>com</u>plaint
com + mander	= <u>com</u>mander	com + plexion	= <u>com</u>plexion

LESSON GENERALIZATION: The prefix **com** means "with" or "together." This prefix can be spelled in two ways, **com** or **con,** depending on the root to which the prefix is joined. Use **com** before roots that begin with the letter **m, p,** or **b. Con** is easier to pronounce before roots beginning with other consonants:

Say com**s**tant. Then say con**s**tant.

A. Complete the following exercises.

1. The prefix **com** does not change its spelling when it comes before word roots beginning with _____, _____ and _____. Write the words from the list in which the spelling of **com** remains unchanged when added to a word root.

_____   _____   _____

_____   _____   _____

_____   _____   _____

_____

2. The prefix **com** is spelled **con** before most letters of the alphabet. Write the words from the word list that begin with **con.**

_____   _____   _____

_____   _____   _____

_____   _____

B. On a separate sheet of paper, write a brief definition of each word in the spelling list.

LESSON 12 MORE PRACTICE
The prefix *com*

1. conjunction
2. convention
3. consider
4. concern
5. constant
6. consent
7. concert
8. congress
9. communication
10. committee
11. commend
12. commence
13. commander
14. combination
15. complicate
16. competition
17. complaint
18. complexion

A. Complete each sentence with words from the spelling list. Do not use a word more than once.

1. The band _____ was about to _____ when the sound system failed.

2. The doctor recommended a special soap to improve my _____ .

3. After an hour of _____ pleading, I convinced my father to give

   his _____ .

4. I would never _____ choosing that odd color for my room.

5. In her written _____ , she did not use a single preposition

   or _____ .

6. Hundreds attended this year's _____ to express

   _____ about the new policy.

7. The _____ of the army did not hear a single _____
   from any soldier.

B. Match each clue with a word from the spelling list. Write the word on the line next to the clue.

1. be of interest to _____

2. assembly of govern- _____
   ment leaders

3. to praise or honor _____

4. a word that joins _____
   other words

5. to make complex _____

6. rivalry or opposition _____

7. musical _____
   performance

8. a union or joining _____
   together

9. a group of appointed _____
   people

10. a statement of _____
    discontent

LESSON 13 TEACHING

Forms of the prefix *ad*

ad + vertise	= advertise		ad + opt	= adopt
ad + just	= adjust		ad + ministrator	= administrator
ad + mire	= admire		ad + dressed	= addressed

ad + pear	= appear		ad + pliance	= appliance
ad + ply	= apply		ad + plication	= application
ad + point	= appoint		ad + proximate	= approximate
ad + plause	= applause		ad + pendix	= appendix
ad + prove	= approve		ad + petite	= appetite
ad + proach	= approach		ad + preciate	= appreciate

LESSON GENERALIZATION: The prefix **ad** means "to" or "toward." This prefix can be spelled in different ways. The spelling depends on the root to which the prefix is joined. The prefix **ad** often changes to match the first letter of a root. It changes to **ap** when the root begins with the letter **p**.

Appetite is easier to pronounce than **adp**etite.

Remember why some of these words have double consonants. One of the letters belongs to the root. One belongs to the prefix.

A. Complete the following exercises.

1. The prefix **ad** changes to _____ when it comes before a word root beginning with the letter **p**. Write the examples from the word list that follow this rule.

_____	_____	_____
_____	_____	_____
_____	_____	_____

2. In most cases, the prefix **ad** does not change when it is added to a word root. Write examples from the word list that follow this rule.

_____	_____
_____	_____

B. On a separate sheet of paper, write a short story using at least ten words from the word list.

LESSON 13 MORE PRACTICE

Forms of the prefix *ad*

1. advertise
2. adjust
3. admire
4. adopt
5. administrator
6. addressed
7. appear
8. apply
9. appoint
10. applause
11. approve
12. approach
13. appliance
14. application
15. approximate
16. appendix
17. appetite
18. appreciate

A. Write the word from the spelling list that fits in each set of boxes.

1.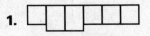

2.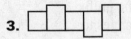

3.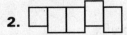

4.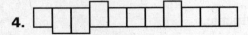

5.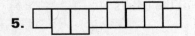

6.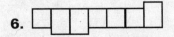

7.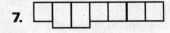

8.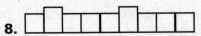

9.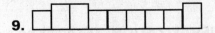

10.

11.

12.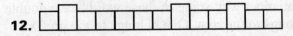

13.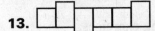

B. Circle the misspelled word in each group. Write it correctly.

1. administrator   apply

   adplause   adventure

   _____

2. appreciate   aproach

   adjust   appear

   _____

3. apreciate   approximate

   appendix   appetite

   _____

4. advertise   admire

   apendix   appoint

   _____

LESSON
14 TEACHING
Words ending with *ory*

fact<u>ory</u>	explanat<u>ory</u>	direct<u>ory</u>
laborat<u>ory</u>	exclamat<u>ory</u>	hist<u>ory</u>
territ<u>ory</u>	audit<u>ory</u>	satisfact<u>ory</u>
explorat<u>ory</u>	introduct<u>ory</u>	preparat<u>ory</u>
vict<u>ory</u>	dormit<u>ory</u>	contradict<u>ory</u>
invent<u>ory</u>	observat<u>ory</u>	deposit<u>ory</u>

LESSON GENERALIZATION: The **ory** suffix often follows the letter **t**. The suffix is easy to hear and identify when pronouncing **ory** words of four or more syllables. In **ory** words of three syllables, careless pronunciation can make the suffix difficult to hear.

say <u>his-tor-y</u> not <u>his-try</u>   say <u>vic-tor-y</u> not <u>vic-try</u>

A. Complete the following exercises.

1. Read carefully each word in the word list. Write the words that have only three syllables.

   _____   _____   _____

2. Write the four-or-more syllable words that have added the **ory** suffix.

   _____   _____   _____

   _____   _____   _____

   _____   _____   _____

   _____   _____   _____

   _____   _____

B. On a separate sheet of paper, identify each **ory** word as a noun or adjective. Some nouns can also be used as adjectives in a sentence (<u>history</u> book), but list the most common form the word takes. Compare your list with a partner's list. Use a dictionary to determine the part of speech for any word on which you do not agree.

LESSON MORE PRACTICE
14 Words ending with *ory*

1. factory
2. laboratory
3. territory
4. exploratory
5. victory
6. inventory

7. explanatory
8. exclamatory
9. auditory
10. introductory
11. dormitory
12. observatory

13. directory
14. history
15. satisfactory
16. preparatory
17. contradictory
18. depository

A. Write the word from the spelling list that fits each definition and fits in the boxes.

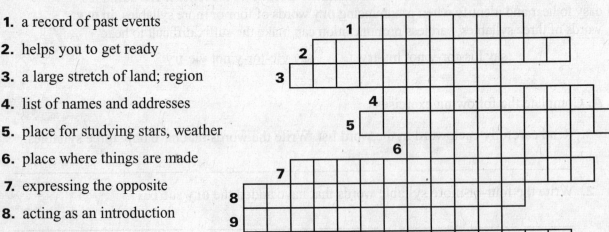

1. a record of past events
2. helps you to get ready
3. a large stretch of land; region
4. list of names and addresses
5. place for studying stars, weather
6. place where things are made
7. expressing the opposite
8. acting as an introduction
9. telling how
10. for exploration
11. home for college students
12. listing of items

What additional word do you find hidden in the boxes? _____

B. For this exercise, use your dictionary or the results from your work on Exercise B on page 195. Write the ten spelling words that can be nouns. Then write the plural form of each.

Noun	Plural		Noun	Plural
1. _____ _____		6. _____ _____
2. _____ _____		7. _____ _____
3. _____ _____		8. _____ _____
4. _____ _____		9. _____ _____
5. _____ _____		10. _____ _____

LESSON 15 TEACHING
Unstressed syllables

sev<u>e</u>ral	prob<u>a</u>bly	comf<u>o</u>rtable
priv<u>i</u>lege	soph<u>o</u>more	rest<u>au</u>rant
diff<u>e</u>rent	pos<u>i</u>tive	temp<u>e</u>rature
gen<u>e</u>rous	int<u>e</u>rest	lit<u>e</u>rature
dec<u>i</u>mal	mem<u>o</u>ry	veg<u>e</u>table
choc<u>o</u>late	caf<u>e</u>teria	math<u>e</u>matics

LESSON GENERALIZATION: The spelling problem in these words is caused by their pronunciation. Some unaccented middle syllables are dropped when the words are spoken. Sometimes the unaccented syllable is easier to hear in another form of the word.

mem<u>o</u>ry: mem<u>o</u>rial   prob<u>a</u>bly: prob<u>a</u>bility

A. Complete the following exercises.

1. Carefully pronounce each word in the word list. Note the underlined letter in each word. These are the letters most frequently left out when one pronounces or spells the words. Are

these letters consonants or vowels? _____

2. Again, pronounce and then write each word from the word list. As you do, pay close attention to the unaccented (the underlined) vowel in each.

_____   _____   _____

_____   _____   _____

_____   _____   _____

_____   _____   _____

_____   _____   _____

_____   _____   _____

B. On a separate sheet of paper, write each word from the word list. Then write another form of as many words as you can. Compare your list to a partner's.

LESSON 15 MORE PRACTICE

Unstressed syllables

SPELLING

1. several	7. probably	13. comfortable
2. privilege	8. sophomore	14. restaurant
3. different	9. positive	15. temperature
4. generous	10. interest	16. literature
5. decimal	11. memory	17. vegetable
6. chocolate	12. cafeteria	18. mathematics

A. Complete the crossword puzzle with words from the list of spelling words.

Across

2. formal eating place

4. study of numbers

10. informal eating area

11. willing to give

12. recall of the past

13. punctuation to show place in numbers

Down

1. a body of writing

3. unusual

5. year between freshman and junior

6. candy made with cocoa

7. likely to occur

8. many

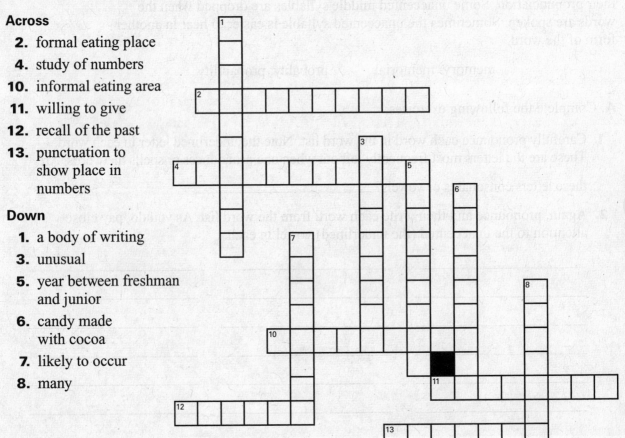

B. Write the word from the spelling list that fits each group of words.

1. curious, concern, regard, _____

2. many, none, few, _____

3. strawberry, vanilla, cherry, _____

4. cozy, easy, snug, _____

5. sure, confident, certain, _____

6. Celsius, Fahrenheit, _____

7. squash, tomato, corn, _____

8. period, dash, comma, _____

LESSON 16 Review

1. employing
2. qualified
3. occupied
4. comfortable
5. valuable
6. reliable
7. usually
8. physically
9. practically
10. nationally
11. consider
12. competition
13. communication
14. combination
15. applause
16. advertise
17. appetite
18. directory
19. history
20. satisfactory
21. several
22. different
23. chocolate
24. temperature
25. probably

A. Complete each analogy with the correct form of a word from the spelling list.

1. **consider** is to **considerable** as **comfort** is to _____

2. **betray** is to **betraying** as **employ** is to _____

3. **combine** is to **combination** as **communicate** is to _____

4. **preparation** is to **preparatory** as **satisfaction** is to _____

5. **general** is to **generally** as **usual** is to _____

6. **deny** is to **denied** as **occupy** is to _____

7. **invent** is to **inventory** as **direct** is to _____

8. **typical** is to **typically** as **practical** is to _____

9. **occupy** is to **occupies** as **qualify** is to _____

10. **vary** is to **variable** as **rely** is to _____

B. Complete each phrase with a word from the list.

competition	valuable	appetite	temperature
reliable	combination	several	physically
advertise	different	chocolate	consider

1. a hearty _____

2. knew _____ of the performers

3. _____ strenuous exercise

4. _____ silver coins

5. the _____ to my lock

6. many _____ types of books

7. hottest _____ this month

8. a _____ ice cream soda

9. _____ between two teams

10. will _____ your request

11. _____ the product on TV

12. a _____ bus schedule

LESSON 16 Review

SPELLING

A. Three words in each row follow the same spelling pattern. One word does not. Circle that word.

1. observatory	memory	preparatory	exploratory
2. notable	taxable	respectable	considerable
3. complicate	combination	commend	consent
4. portrayed	occupied	employed	betrayed
5. commend	commence	communication	convention
6. factories	remedies	surveys	ceremonies
7. appear	apply	approve	admire
8. factually	occasionally	probably	accidentally
9. predictable	questionable	favorable	valuable
10. several	different	interest	appendix

B. Complete each analogy using a word from the list.

remedy	approximate	restaurant	verbally	commence
valuable	complicated	chocolate	denied	employs

1. thinking is to **mentally** as **speaking** is to _____

2. finish is to **end** as **begin** is to _____

3. easy is to **simple** as **difficult** is to _____

4. praise is to **flattery** as **cure** is to _____

5. consented is to **approved** as **refused** is to _____

6. deliberate is to **accidentally** as **worthless** is to _____

7. student is to **sophomore** as **flavor** is to _____

8. beds is to **dormitory** as **food** is to _____

9. fires is to **dismisses** as **hires** is to _____

10. exact is to **specific** as **almost** is to _____

Name _____ Date _____

refer	→ referred	referring	refers
prefer	→ preferred	preferring	prefers
occur	→ occurrence	occurring	occurs
commit	→ committed	committing	commits
forbid	→ forbidden	forbidding	forbids
confer	→ conferred	conferring	confers
rebel	→ rebellion	rebelling	rebels
transfer	→ transferred	transferring	transfers

LESSON GENERALIZATION: A **VAC** word has a single **v**owel before a single **c**onsonant in an **a**ccented final syllable. Double the final consonant of a **VAC** word before adding a suffix that begins with a vowel. Do not double the final consonant before adding a suffix that begins with a consonant.

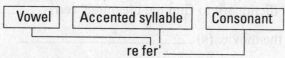

```
    Vowel    Accented syllable    Consonant
              re fer'
```

A. Complete the following exercises.

1. Circle the correct word or phrase in the following statement.

(Double/Do not double) the final consonant of a **VAC** word before a suffix beginning with a vowel.

Write the words from the list that end in a suffix beginning with a vowel.

_____ _____ _____ _____

_____ _____ _____ _____

_____ _____ _____ _____

2. Circle the correct word of phrase in the following statement.

(Double/Do not double) the final consonant of a **VAC** word before a suffix beginning with a consonant.

Write the words from the list that follow this rule.

_____ _____ _____ _____

_____ _____ _____ _____

B. On a separate sheet of paper, write eight sets of original sentences. For each verb in the first column of the spelling list, write three sentences, one with each form of the verb listed in the second, third, and forth columns of the spelling list.

LESSON
17 *VAC* **words**

referred	referring	refers
referred	preferring	prefers
occurrence	occurring	occurs
committed	committing	commits
forbidden	forbidding	forbids
conferred	conferring	confers
rebellion	rebelling	rebels
transferred	transferring	transfers

A. Add the suffix in parentheses to the underlined word and write it on the line.

1. A mistake <u>occur</u> in your spelling. **(s)** _____

2. Are you <u>forbid</u> from wearing jeans to class? **(en)** _____

3. Have you <u>refer</u> to your dictionary to find the meaning? **(ed)** _____

4. Jan <u>prefer</u> the book to the movie. **(s)** _____

5. You <u>confer</u> with the coach. **(ed)** _____

6. Unfair taxes caused the colonists' <u>rebel</u>. **(ion)** _____

7. The suspect <u>commit</u> the crime. **(ed)** _____

8. Tim <u>transfer</u> to a new school. **(ed)** _____

B. Circle the eight words from the spelling list in the word search puzzle. Words are horizontally foward and backward. Some words may overlap.

F	U	D	E	R	R	E	F	E	R	K	C
G	N	I	R	R	E	F	S	N	A	R	T
P	R	E	F	E	R	R	I	N	G	N	O
R	G	N	I	D	D	I	B	R	O	F	S
E	S	R	E	F	N	O	C	C	U	R	S
C	O	M	M	I	T	T	E	D	T	R	R
U	N	N	O	I	L	L	E	B	E	R	L

LESSON 18
Non-*VAC* words

travel	→	traveled	traveling	travels
label	→	labeled	labeling	labels
model	→	modeled	modeling	models
cancel	→	canceled	canceling	cancels
panel	→	paneled	paneling	panels
edit	→	editor	editing	edits
credit	→	credited	crediting	credits
profit	→	profitable	profiting	profits

LESSON GENERALIZATION: Some base words that end in a single vowel before a single consonant do not have a final accented syllable. Do not double the final consonant before adding a suffix to these words.

A. Complete the following exercises.

1. If a word ends in a single vowel before a single consonant, but the final syllable is not accented, what happens to the final consonant when a suffix is added?

   _____

2. Write the non-**VAC** words from the list that have an added suffix.

   _____   _____   _____

   _____   _____   _____

   _____   _____   _____

   _____   _____   _____

   _____   _____   _____

   _____   _____   _____

   _____   _____   _____

B. On a separate sheet of paper, alphabetize all words from the list that have a suffix ending.

SPELLING

LESSON 18 MORE PRACTICE
Non-*VAC* words

1. traveled	7. modeled	13. paneled	19. credited
2. traveling	8. modeling	14. paneling	20. crediting
3. travels	9. models	15. panels	21. credits
4. labeled	10. canceled	16. editor	22. profitable
5. labeling	11. canceling	17. editing	23. profiting
6. labels	12. cancels	18. edits	24. profits

A. Complete each sentence with two different forms of a spelling word.

1. Juanita takes a course in _____ so she can work with fashion _____.

2. Our garage sale was so _____ that we split the _____ three ways.

3. I am used to _____ by car since I have _____ from Maine to Oregon.

4. The _____ of the magazine may suggest further _____ of your story.

5. Did you have _____ for the package, or was it _____ by the post office?

6. We are _____ our plans if the picnic has been _____ because of rain.

7. The wood _____ in the office needs to be _____ again.

8. The recent _____ to your account have not yet been _____.

B. Write the spelling words that match the clues and fit in the puzzle. Each word should use the same suffix that is underlined in the clue.

Across

1. cover<u>ed</u> with sheets of wood

3. give<u>s</u> recognition to

5. display<u>s</u> clothes

6. supervi<u>sor</u> of a newspaper

Down

1. cap<u>able</u> of making money

2. name ta<u>gs</u>

3. call<u>ed</u> off

4. goe<u>s</u> from place to place

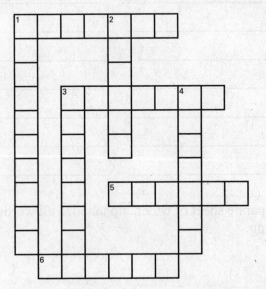

LESSON
19 Words ending with *c + ally*

realistic	+ ally =	realistically	rhythmic + ally =	rhythmically
historic	+ ally =	historically	magic + ally =	magically
athletic	+ ally =	athletically	comic + ally =	comically
logic	+ ally =	logically	music + ally =	musically
electric	+ ally =	electrically	mechanic + ally =	mechanically
patriotic	+ ally =	patriotically	artistic + ally =	artistically
critic	+ ally =	critically	tropic + ally =	tropically
apologetic	+ ally =	apologetically	sarcastic + ally =	sarcastically
basic	+ ally =	basically	tragic + ally =	tragically

LESSON GENERALIZATION: Words that end with the letter **c** use the ending **ally.**
Do not add **ly** directly to the letter **c.**

A. Complete the following exercises.

1. Nouns and adjectives that end in **ic** can be made into adjectives and adverbs by

adding the suffix _____ .

2. Write the words from the word list that end in **ically.**

_____   _____   _____

_____   _____   _____

_____   _____   _____

_____   _____   _____

_____   _____   _____

_____   _____   _____

B. On a separate sheet of paper, use each word from the spelling list in an
original sentence.

LESSON 19 MORE PRACTICE
Words ending with c + ally

1. realistically
2. historically
3. athletically
4. logically
5. electrically
6. patriotically
7. critically
8. apologetically
9. basically
10. rhythmically
11. magically
12. comically
13. musically
14. mechanically
15. artistically
16. tropically
17. sarcastically
18. tragically

A. Make a spelling word from the scrambled syllables in each group.

1. cal i crit ly _____
2. cal ot pa i ly tri _____
3. chan ly i me cal _____
4. tri ly lec e cal _____
5. cal pol i get o a ly _____
6. ti ly ar tis cal _____
7. si cal ly mu _____
8. let ly cal i ath _____
9. cal rhyth ly mi _____
10. tor ly i his cal _____
11. al re ti is ly cal _____
12. ly i trag cal _____
13. cal ly mag i _____
14. cal com i ly _____
15. si cal ba ly _____
16. ti cas ly sar cal _____
17. cal i ly trop _____
18. ly cal log i _____

B. Write the word that matches each clue.

1. mainly _____
2. automatically _____
3. having to do with art _____
4. in a way that shows love of country _____
5. having to do with criticism _____
6. in a mocking way _____
7. dealing with electricity _____
8. seeing things as they are _____
9. in a way that shows you are sorry _____
10. dealing with rhythm _____

LESSON
20 TEACHING
The prefix *ex*

ex + tract	= extract		ex + pect	= expect
ex + tra	= extra		ex + pense	= expense
ex + treme	= extreme		ex + periment	= experiment
ex + tent	= extent		ex + perience	= experience
ex + terior	= exterior		ex + piration	= expiration
ex + ternal	= external		ex + pert	= expert
ex + tinguish	= extinguish		ex + pedition	= expedition
ex + terminate	= exterminate		ex + pression	= expression
ex + travagant	= extravagant		ex + plode	= explode

LESSON GENERALIZATION: The prefix **ex** means "out" or "beyond." It is added directly to roots beginning with the letters **t** or **p**. The letter **x** is never doubled. Words beginning with the letters **exs** are not commonly used. The letter **x** itself makes the sound of **s** or **z**.

A. Complete the following exercises.

1. Add the **ex** prefix directly to roots beginning with the letters _____

   and _____ . Never double the letter **x**.

2. Write the words from the spelling list in which the prefix **ex** is followed by **t**.

   _____ _____ _____

   _____ _____ _____

   _____ _____ _____

3. Write the words from the list in which the prefix **ex** is followed by **p**.

   _____ _____ _____

   _____ _____ _____

   _____ _____ _____

B. On a separate sheet of paper, write a story of the "exes." Use as many words from the spelling list as you can, and use your imagination.

LESSON
20 MORE PRACTICE
The prefix *ex*

1. extract	7. extinguish	13. experience
2. extra	8. exterminate	14. expiration
3. extreme	9. extravagant	15. expert
4. extent	10. expect	16. expedition
5. exterior	11. expense	17. expression
6. external	12. experiment	18. explode

A. Complete the sentences with words from the spelling list. Three list words are used in each sentence. No word is used more than once.

1. The _____ of painting the _____ of the old

   house would be costly and foolishly _____.

2. The _____ from the oil company described the

   _____ his company was conducting to _____

   oil from beneath the sea.

3. The _____ of the _____ damage was slight, but

   the inside of the building was nearly destroyed before the firemen could

   _____ the flames.

4. The _____ cold required the members of the arctic

   _____ to wear _____ layers of clothing.

5. Judging by the _____ on his face, he did not consider it a pleasant

   _____ to _____ the rodents.

6. Does the grocer _____ the cans of food to _____

   when they are kept past their _____ date?

B. First, write the only spelling word that
fits in the shaded boxes. Then write ten more
words to fit in the boxes across. Use the shaded
word as a clue to the others.

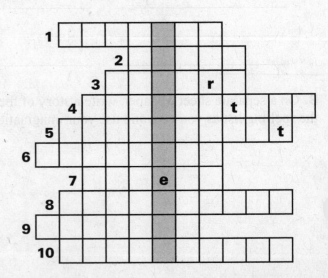

LESSON 21 TEACHING

More forms of the prefix *ad*

ad + tack = at̲tack	ad + cuse = ac̲cuse
ad + tend = at̲tend	ad + curate = ac̲curate
ad + tempt = at̲tempt	ad + commodate = ac̲commodate
ad + tract = at̲tract	ad + company = ac̲company
ad + tach = at̲tach	ad + cumulate = ac̲cumulate
ad + tention = at̲tention	ad + celerate = ac̲celerate
ad + titude = at̲titude	ad + cented = ac̲cented
ad + quaint = ac̲quaint	ad + customed = ac̲customed
ad + quire = ac̲quire	ad + complished = ac̲complished

LESSON GENERALIZATION: The adaptable **ad** changes before the letters **t, c,** and **q.** The prefix **ad** becomes **at** before roots that begin with the letter **t.** It becomes **ac** before roots that begin with a **c** or a **q.** Remember why some of these words have double consonants. One of the letters belongs to the root. One belongs to the prefix.

A. Complete the following exercises.

1. The prefix **ad** becomes _____ before roots that begin with the letter **t.** Write the words from the spelling list that follow this rule.

   _____   _____   _____

   _____   _____   _____

   _____

2. The prefix **ad** becomes _____ before roots that begin with the letter **q** or **c.** Write the words from the spelling list that follow this rule.

   _____   _____   _____

   _____   _____   _____

   _____   _____   _____

   _____

B. On a separate sheet of paper, make a word search using all of the words from the spelling list. Trade puzzles with a partner and solve your partner's word search.

LESSON 21 MORE PRACTICE

More forms or the prefix *ad*

1. attack	7. attitude	13. accelerate
2. attend	8. accuse	14. accented
3. attempt	9. accurate	15. accustomed
4. attract	10. accommodate	16. accomplished
5. attach	11. accompany	17. acquaint
6. attention	12. accumulate	18. acquire

A. Unscramble the syllables to make spelling words. Some groups contain one or two extra syllables.

1. tempt cent ad at _____

2. ti at ten tude _____

3. at ding ad tach _____

4. cum late u ac _____

5. ten tion ac quaint _____

6. ad cur ate ac _____

7. tion at ti ten _____

8. ac mo com date _____

9. com ad ac plished _____

10. ate er cel ac _____

11. tract cur at ti _____

12. late cuse ac com _____

13. cel ac ton quire _____

14. tend trac at ad _____

15. com y ac pan _____

16. tomed cus ion ac _____

17. at ed cent ac _____

18. ad tack at ire _____

B. Write the spelling word that is the synonym (S) or antonym (A) for each word below.

1. discard (A) _____

2. try (S) _____

3. introduce (S) _____

4. blame (S) _____

5. hurry (S) _____

6. repel (A) _____

7. stressed (S) _____

8. adjust (S) _____

9. indifference (A) _____

10. opinion (S) _____

11. give (A) _____

12. inexact (A) _____

13. escort (S) _____

14. unaccustomed (A) _____

Name _____   Date _____

LESSON
22 TEACHING
Base word changes

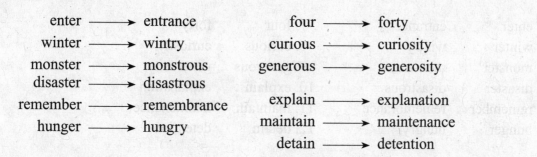

enter ⟶ entrance
winter ⟶ wintry
monster ⟶ monstrous
disaster ⟶ disastrous
remember ⟶ remembrance
hunger ⟶ hungry

four ⟶ forty
curious ⟶ curiosity
generous ⟶ generosity
explain ⟶ explanation
maintain ⟶ maintenance
detain ⟶ detention

LESSON GENERALIZATION: A few common words change the spelling of the base word in an unusual way when a suffix is added. These unexpected spellings result from dropped or changed vowels.

disast**er** ⟶ disast**rous**   hung**er** ⟶ hung**ry**

A. Complete the following exercises.

1. Some base words change form when a suffix is added. When a suffix is added to a word from the first group, what happens to the **er**?

_____

Write the **er** words from the list that follow this pattern.

_____ ⟶ _____   _____ ⟶ _____

_____ ⟶ _____   _____ ⟶ _____

_____ ⟶ _____   _____ ⟶ _____

2. When a suffix is added to a word from the second group, what happens to the **ou**?

_____

Write the words from the list that follow this pattern.

_____ ⟶ _____   _____ ⟶ _____

_____ ⟶ _____

3. When a suffix is added to a word from the third group, how does the **ai** change?

_____ or _____.

Write the words from this group.

_____ ⟶ _____   _____ ⟶ _____

_____ ⟶ _____

B. On a separate sheet of paper, write 12 sentences. Use one word pair in each.

LESSON 22 MORE PRACTICE

Base word changes

SPELLING

1. enter	entrance	7. four	forty
2. winter	wintry	8. curious	curiosity
3. monster	monstrous	9. generous	generosity
4. disaster	disastrous	10. explain	explanation
5. remember	remembrance	11. maintain	maintenance
6. hunger	hungry	12. detain	detention

A. Complete each sentence with a spelling word.

1. Although it was January, the weather did not seem _____.

2. The bus couldn't go through the tunnel because the _____ was closed.

3. Although we'd never forget our trip, we bought postcards as a _____.

4. The food sent to the _____ flood victims was immensely helpful.

5. We hired a _____ crew to take care of the building.

6. The police will hold the suspects in a _____ cell overnight.

7. I tried to help him understand, but my _____ was not clear enough.

8. Marie's _____ is appreciated by those she helps.

9. If you save ten dollars for four weeks, you will have _____ dollars.

10. The severe storm was not as _____ as the following earthquake.

B. Write the spelling words that match the clues and fit in the puzzle.

Across

4. a desire to know
6. cold and icy
8. recollection
9. unselfish
10. doorway
11. interpretation

Down

1. needing food
2. two twenties
3. upkeep
5. unnatural
7. confinement

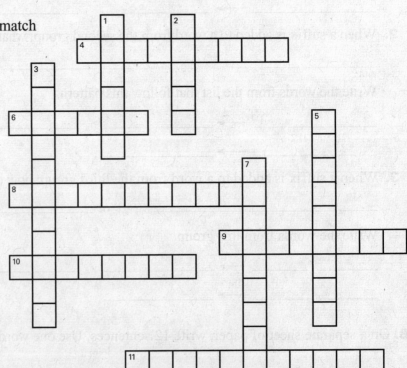

LESSON
23 TEACHING
Words ending with *cious, cial,* or *cian*

suspi<u>cious</u>	finan<u>cial</u>	physi<u>cian</u>
deli<u>cious</u>	artifi<u>cial</u>	politi<u>cian</u>
vi<u>cious</u>	spe<u>cial</u>	magi<u>cian</u>
pre<u>cious</u>	ra<u>cial</u>	musi<u>cian</u>
uncons<u>cious</u>	commer<u>cial</u>	pediatri<u>cian</u>
gra<u>cious</u>	so<u>cial</u>	electri<u>cian</u>

LESSON GENERALIZATION: The letters **ci** spell the **/sh/** sound in the syllables **cious, cial,** and **cian.**

suspicious   financial   physician

A. Complete the following exercises.

1. Pronounce all of the words in the word list. What sound does the **ci** make in each

word? _____

2. Write all of the words ending in **cious.**

_____   _____   _____

_____   _____   _____

3. Write the words from the word list that end in **cial.**

_____   _____   _____

_____   _____   _____

4. Write the words that end in **cian.**

_____   _____   _____

_____   _____   _____

B. On a separate sheet of paper, write the words from the spelling list
in alphabetical order.

LESSON 23 MORE PRACTICE

Words ending with *cious, cial,* or *cian*

1. suspicious
2. delicious
3. vicious
4. precious
5. unconscious

6. gracious
7. financial
8. artificial
9. special
10. racial

11. commercial
12. social
13. physician
14. politician
15. magician

16. musician
17. pediatrician
18. electrician

A. Write an answer for each question, using one of the words from the spelling list. The underlined words will help you decide which words to choose.

1. Was the room decorated with <u>fake</u> flowers?

_____

2. When did Dad take Joey to the <u>children's doctor</u>?

_____

3. Is Ms. Jones <u>active in politics</u>?

_____

4. Does Tom's father <u>repair electrical equipment</u>?

_____

5. Does Billy <u>play the flute</u> well?

_____

6. Wasn't that <u>advertisement</u> effective?

_____

7. Is gold or silver the more <u>valuable</u> metal?

_____

8. Which person <u>performed the magic tricks</u>?

_____

9. Has the theater gone bankrupt because of problems <u>with money</u>?

_____

10. Should all governments strive for equality <u>among races</u>?

_____

B. On a separate sheet of paper, create a word search using all of the words in the spelling list. Trade papers with a partner and solve each other's puzzles.

LESSON 24 Review

1. referred
2. forbidden
3. occurring
4. conferring
5. canceled
6. credited
7. profitable
8. realistically
9. athletically
10. basically
11. magically
12. extra
13. expect
14. expense
15. attention
16. accumulate
17. acquire
18. forty
19. hungry
20. maintenance
21. curiosity
22. detention
23. delicious
24. special
25. physician

A. Complete each analogy with the correct form of a word from the spelling list.

1. **model** is to **modeling** as **credit** is to _____

2. **prefer** is to **preferred** as **refer** is to _____

3. **explain** is to **explanation** as **detain** is to _____

4. **commit** is to **committing** as **occur** is to _____

5. **magical** is to **magician** as **physical** is to _____

6. **remember** is to **remembrance** as **maintain** is to _____

7. **winter** is to **wintry** as **hunger** is to _____

8. **comic** is to **comically** as **realistic** is to _____

9. **generous** is to **generosity** as **curious** is to _____

10. **critic** is to **critically** as **basic** is to _____

B. Complete each phrase with a word from the list.

magically	occurrence	forty	conferred
expect	acquire	credit	accumulate
attention	profitable	detention	referring

1. got the crowd's _____

2. a _____ fund-raising event

3. didn't _____ to win

4. owned _____ acres of land

5. used a _____ card

6. _____ made a rabbit disappear

7. _____ a pile of newspapers

8. the _____ of the prisoner

9. hope to _____ more stamps

10. not an everyday _____

11. is _____ her to a good doctor

12. _____ with the committee members

SPELLING

LESSON 24 Review

A. Follow the directions to make related forms of spelling words. Remember spelling rules you've learned.

1. acquire	change **ac** to **re**	and	add **ment**	_____
2. attract	change **at** to **dis**	and	add **ion**	_____
3. accurate	change **te** to **cy**	and	add **in**	_____
4. extinguish	change **ex** to **dis**	and	add **ed**	_____
5. external	change **ex** to **in**	and	add **ly**	_____
6. precious	change **ous** to **ate**	and	add **ap**	_____
7. artificial	change **arti** to **of**	and	add **ly**	_____
8. explanation	take off **ex** and **ation**	and	add **ing**	_____
9. expense	change **ex** to **com**	and	add **ation**	_____
10. unconscious	take off **un**	and	add **ly**	_____

B. Three words in each row follow the same spelling pattern. Circle the word that does not follow the pattern.

1.	vicious	disastrous	precious	delicious
2.	musician	magician	pediatrician	attention
3.	expert	expedition	entrance	experience
4.	committing	conferring	rebelling	crediting
5.	attitude	accurate	accompany	accent
6.	traveled	preferred	profited	paneled
7.	patriotically	rhythmically	mechanically	curiously
8.	attempt	accomplished	attract	attack
9.	external	racial	commercial	financial
10.	credited	edited	occurred	labeled

LESSON 25 TEACHING

Greek combining forms

astro	+ naut	= astronaut		dia	+ gram	= diagram
astro	+ logy	= astrology		mono	+ gram	= monogram
eco	+ logy	= ecology		tele	+ gram	= telegram
bio	+ logy	= biology		tele	+ photo	= telephoto
mytho	+ logy	= mythology		photo	+ graph	= photograph
peri	+ scope	= periscope		syn	+ onym	= synonym
peri	+ meter	= perimeter		hom	+ onym	= homonym
thermo	+ meter	= thermometer		aristo	+ cracy	= aristocracy
dia	+ meter	= diameter		demo	+ cracy	= democracy

LESSON GENERALIZATION: Greek word parts or forms can be combined in different ways to make English words. They are joined in almost the same way English words are joined to make compound words:

Combined Greek forms	English compound words
telephoto, photograph	touchdown, downstairs

Knowing the meaning of the separate parts will help you to understand the many words made by combining the parts.

A. Complete the following exercises.

1. Read the list of Greek combining forms. Notice that some parts most often appear at the ends of words and others are found at the beginning. What Greek word part is used at both

   the beginning and end of a word? _____

2. Write the words that are made by combining Greek word parts.

   _____ _____ _____

   _____ _____ _____

   _____ _____ _____

   _____ _____ _____

   _____ _____ _____

B. On a separate sheet of paper, write a brief definition for each word from the word list.

LESSON 25 MORE PRACTICE

Greek combining forms

SPELLING

1. astronaut
2. astrology
3. ecology
4. biology
5. mythology
6. periscope
7. perimeter
8. thermometer
9. diameter
10. diagram
11. monogram
12. telegram
13. telephoto
14. photograph
15. synonym
16. homonym
17. aristocracy
18. democracy

A. Complete each sentence with the correct word from the word list.

1. The submarine sailors used a _____ to see above water.

2. The line through the center of a circle is called the _____.

3. We learned about frog development in our _____ class.

4. Marta sewed a _____ onto her sweater.

5. Which _____ first set foot on the moon?

6. He used a _____ lens on the camera to get that shot.

7. The word *dangerous* is a _____ for the word *hazardous*.

8. On a Celsius _____, 0 degrees is freezing.

9. Randi took a _____ of the magnificent waterfall.

10. People who follow _____ believe that the planets and stars affect our lives.

11. Mark drew a _____ of his invention.

12. Words that are pronounced the same but spelled differently are called

_____.

13. As pollution increases, people become more concerned with _____.

14. We sent a _____ to my aunt on her birthday.

15. Isabel used string to help her measure the _____ of the desk.

16. In a _____, every citizen has a duty to vote.

17. Zeus and Hera are characters in Greek _____.

18. A government ruled by an elite few is known as an _____.

B. On a separate sheet of paper, use each Greek word part from this lesson to create a word not in the spelling list. Compare your list to a partner's list.

Compound words and contractions

does + not	=	doesn't
should + have	=	should've
could + have	=	could've
she + would	=	she'd
who + will	=	who'll
where + is	=	where's

ninety + nine	=	ninety-nine
sister + in + law	=	sister-in-law
right + handed	=	right-handed
double + header	=	double-header
three + eighths	=	three-eighths
half + hour	=	half-hour

hitch + hike	=	hitchhike
touch + down	=	touchdown
head + light	=	headlight

over + rated	=	overrated
wind + shield	=	windshield
wheel + chair	=	wheelchair

LESSON GENERALIZATION: Words can be joined together in several ways. When an apostrophe is used to show that one or more letters have been omitted, the word is called a **contraction**.

doesn't   where's

When two or more words are simply connected with no changes, the word is called a **compound word**. Words joined by a hyphen are another kind of compound word.

touchdown   ninety-five

A. Complete the following exercises.

1. In a contraction, an _____ replaces a missing letter or letters. Write the contractions from the word list.

_____ _____ _____

_____ _____ _____

2. Some compound words are formed when two words are joined without changes to either word. Write the compound words from the list that follow this pattern.

_____ _____ _____

_____ _____ _____

3. In some compound words, the words are joined by a _____. Write the words from the word list that follow this pattern.

_____ _____ _____

_____ _____ _____

B. On a separate sheet of paper, use at least 12 words from the word list in a short story.

LESSON 26 MORE PRACTICE

Compound words and contractions

1. doesn't	7. hitchhike	13. ninety-nine
2. should've	8. touchdown	14. sister-in-law
3. could've	9. headlight	15. right-handed
4. she'd	10. overrated	16. double-header
5. who'll	11. windshield	17. three-eighths
6. where's	12. wheelchair	18. half-hour

A. Write the spelling word that matches each clue. Include hyphens and apostrophes.

1. used in a hospital _____

2. where is _____

3. action in a football game _____

4. two games on the same day _____

5. who will _____

6. glass in car window _____

7. could have _____

8. she would _____

9. my brother's wife _____

10. should have _____

11. too highly thought of _____

12. 100 − 1 = _____

13. travel by asking for rides _____

14. favors right hand _____

15. three parts of eight _____

B. The parts of your spelling words are mixed in the list below to make nonsense words. Match the parts correctly and write them on a separate sheet of paper under these headings: Words with Hyphens; Compound Words; and Contractions.

couldinlaw	shouldrated	touchshield	doeslight
doublenine	sisterdown	windwill	hitchhanded
righthave	ninetyhike	overeighths	threeheader
headwould	wheelis	shenot	whohave
wherehour	halfchair		

LESSON 27 TEACHING
The suffix *ible*

poss<u>ible</u>	ed<u>ible</u>	indel<u>ible</u>
permiss<u>ible</u>	elig<u>ible</u>	incred<u>ible</u>
admiss<u>ible</u>	intellig<u>ible</u>	inflex<u>ible</u>
invis<u>ible</u>	tang<u>ible</u>	terr<u>ible</u>
divis<u>ible</u>	dirig<u>ible</u>	horr<u>ible</u>
leg<u>ible</u>	aud<u>ible</u>	combust<u>ible</u>

LESSON GENERALIZATION: The suffix **ible** is more commonly used with roots than with complete words. It often follows the letter **s** or the soft **g** sound.

Remember: the hard sound of **c** or **g** is usually followed by the suffix **able.** The suffix **able** is commonly used with complete words.

A. Complete each of the following exercises.

1. Note that the suffix **ible** more often follows roots than complete words. It often follows the letter **s.** Write examples of this spelling pattern from the word list.

   _____   _____   _____

   _____   _____

2. The suffix ible also follows a soft **g.** Write examples of this spelling pattern from the word list.

   _____   _____   _____

   _____   _____

3. Write the remaining words from the word list that end in **ible.**

   _____   _____   _____

   _____   _____   _____

   _____   _____

B. On a separate sheet of paper, use each word from the spelling list in an original sentence. Underline the spelling words. Share your sentences with a partner.

SPELLING

1. possible
2. permissible
3. admissible
4. invisible
5. divisible
6. legible
7. eligible
8. intelligible
9. tangible
10. dirigible
11. edible
12. audible
13. indelible
14. incredible
15. inflexible
16. terrible
17. horrible
18. combustible

A. Write the missing letters for each spelling word.

1. h ____ r ____ i ____ l ____

2. a ____ m ____ s ____ i ____ l ____

3. i ____ d ____ l ____ b ____ e

4. e ____ i ____ i ____ l ____

5. d ____ v ____ s ____ b ____ e

6. i ____ v ____ s ____ b ____ e

7. t ____ n ____ i ____ l ____

8. c ____ m ____ u ____ t ____ b ____ e

9. p ____ r ____ i ____ s ____ b ____ e

10. t ____ r ____ i ____ l ____

11. e ____ i ____ l ____

12. i ____ f ____ e ____ i ____ l ____

13. i ____ c ____ e ____ i ____ l ____

14. l ____ g ____ b ____ e

B. Circle the eleven spelling words in this word search maze. They are forward, backward, and downward.

I	N	D	E	L	I	B	L	E	K	K	Z
S	D	F	D	I	V	I	S	I	B	L	E
E	L	B	I	X	E	L	F	N	I	N	L
E	L	B	I	S	S	I	M	R	E	P	B
E	L	B	I	G	I	L	L	E	T	N	I
S	D	I	R	I	G	I	B	L	E	M	S
A	D	M	I	S	S	I	B	L	E	T	I
I	N	C	R	E	D	I	B	L	E	F	V
I	N	G	E	L	B	I	S	S	O	P	N
E	L	B	I	T	S	U	B	M	O	C	I

LESSON 28 TEACHING
Forms of the prefixes *ob* and *sub*

ob + struct	=	<u>obstruct</u>	sub + stitute	=	<u>substitute</u>
ob + ject	=	<u>object</u>	sub + marine	=	<u>submarine</u>
ob + tain	=	<u>obtain</u>	sub + urban	=	<u>suburban</u>
ob + serve	=	<u>observe</u>	sub + traction	=	<u>subtraction</u>
ob + pose	=	<u>oppose</u>	sub + pose	=	<u>suppose</u>
ob + cupy	=	<u>occupy</u>	sub + plies	=	<u>supplies</u>
ob + casion	=	<u>occasion</u>	sub + cessful	=	<u>successful</u>
ob + ficial	=	<u>official</u>	sub + ficient	=	<u>sufficient</u>
ob + fered	=	<u>offered</u>	sub + gestion	=	<u>suggestion</u>

LESSON GENERALIZATION: The prefix **ob** means "against" or "in the way of."
The prefix **sub** means "under," "below," or "in place of." Each of these prefixes can be
spelled in different ways. The spelling depends on the roots to which the prefix is joined.

The letter **b** in the prefixes **ob** and **sub** often changes to blend more easily with the
first letter of a root. When it changes to match the letters **p, c, f,** and **g,** the result is
a double consonant. Remember that one of the double letters in these spelling words
is a **b** in disguise.

oppose   sufficient   suggestion

A. Complete the following exercises.

1. The letter **b** in the prefixes **ob** and **sub** often changes to match the first letter of roots
   beginning with **p, c, f,** and **g.** Write the words from the spelling list that are examples of
   this spelling pattern.

   _____ _____ _____

   _____ _____ _____

   _____ _____ _____

   _____

2. Write the words from the list in which the prefixes **ob** and **sub** do not change form when
   they are joined to the roots.

   _____ _____ _____

   _____ _____ _____

   _____ _____

B. On a separate sheet of paper, create a word search puzzle using at least 12 words
from the spelling list. Trade papers with a partner and solve your partner's puzzle.

SPELLING

28 Forms of the prefixes *ob* and *sub*

1. obstruct	7. occasion	13. subtraction
2. object	8. official	14. suppose
3. obtain	9. offered	15. supplies
4. observe	10. substitute	16. successful
5. oppose	11. submarine	17. sufficient
6. occupy	12. suburban	18. suggestion

A. Unscramble the syllables to make spelling words. There are one or more extra syllables in each group.

1. tri ges tion sug _____

2. rine ev ma sub _____

3. fi tro of cial _____

4. py sti cu oc _____

5. ban sub re ur _____

6. lit ject tri ob _____

7. lit pose reg sup _____

8. sti li tute sub _____

9. cian plies sup ly _____

10. tri pose cial op _____

11. stri struct pre ob _____

12. fi suf ply cient _____

13. tain mis ob cur _____

14. ful mar cess suc _____

15. serve lit ob tab _____

16. ca sion ful oc _____

17. tion fered of _____

18. trac un sub tion _____

B. Rewrite each phrase using a spelling word in place of the underlined words.

1. <u>as much</u> wood <u>as we will need</u> _____

2. celebrate the <u>particular event</u> _____

3. <u>block</u> our view of the contest _____

4. studying <u>under the sea</u> life _____

5. <u>watch</u> the birds building a nest _____

6. <u>on the outskirts of the city of</u> Columbus _____

7. <u>person holding a high office</u> in the bank _____

8. <u>furnishes</u> what is needed _____

9. <u>replacement</u> teacher _____

10. <u>get</u> her passport for the trip _____

LESSON 29 TEACHING
Forms of the prefix *in*

in + patient	= impatient	in + mature	= immature
in + perfect	= imperfect	in + mortal	= immortal
in + practical	= impractical	in + movable	= immovable
in + personal	= impersonal	in + regular	= irregular
in + pure	= impure	in + responsible	= irresponsible
in + proper	= improper	in + resistible	= irresistible
in + prison	= imprison	in + legal	= illegal
in + print	= imprint	in + legible	= illegible
in + press	= impress	in + literate	= illiterate

LESSON GENERALIZATION: The prefix **in** has two common meanings. It may mean "in or into," or it may mean "not or without." The prefix may be spelled in different ways. The spelling depends on the root to which the prefix is joined.

The prefix **in** is spelled **im** before base words that begin with the letters **m** or **p.** It changes to **ir** before the letter **r.** It changes to **il** before the letter **l.** Remember the double consonants when you spell these words.

impatient irregular illegal

A. Complete the following exercises.

1. The prefix **in** is spelled _____ before base words that begin with **m** or **p.** Write the words from the word list that follow this pattern.

_____ _____ _____

_____ _____ _____

_____ _____ _____

_____ _____

2. The prefix **in** is spelled _____ before base words that begin with **r.** Write the words from the list that follow this pattern.

_____ _____ _____

3. The prefix **in** is spelled _____ before base words that begin with **l.** Write the words from the list that follow this pattern.

_____ _____ _____

B. On a separate sheet of paper, write a brief definition for each spelling word.

LESSON 29 MORE PRACTICE

Forms of the prefix *in*

1. impatient
2. imperfect
3. impractical
4. impersonal
5. impure
6. improper
7. imprison
8. imprint
9. impress
10. immature
11. immortal
12. immovable
13. irregular
14. irresponsible
15. irresistible
16. illegal
17. illegible
18. illiterate

A. Write the spelling word that means the opposite of each clue.

1. allowed by law _____

2. useful _____

3. can be moved _____

4. educated _____

5. usual _____

6. have no effect on _____

7. able to put up with delay _____

8. unappealing _____

9. fully grown _____

10. won't live forever _____

11. faultless _____

12. set free _____

13. respectable _____

14. easy to read _____

15. private or specific _____

16. showing a sense of duty _____

17. clean _____

18. to remove a mark _____

B. Write the spelling word that matches each clue and fits the puzzle.

Across

3. firmly fixed
7. not fully grown
8. not clean
9. not usual
10. not educated
11. not practical
12. against the law

Down

1. not suitable
2. having a fault or flaw
4. too strong to resist
5. living forever
6. not patient

LESSON 30 TEACHING
The suffixes *ence* and *ent*

aud<u>ience</u>	influ<u>ence</u>	presid<u>ent</u>
obed<u>ience</u>	evid<u>ence</u>	frequ<u>ent</u>
viol<u>ence</u>	interfer<u>ence</u>	delinqu<u>ent</u>
sil<u>ence</u>	circumfer<u>ence</u>	
abs<u>ence</u>	differ<u>ence</u>	
pres<u>ence</u>	coincid<u>ence</u>	
pat<u>ience</u>	sci<u>ence</u>	
intellig<u>ence</u>		

LESSON GENERALIZATION: The suffixes **ence** and **ent** are commonly added to roots. They are often used after the letters **fer** and **qu.**

interference   frequent

A. Complete the following exercises.

1. The suffixes **ence** and **ent** often follow roots ending in the letters

   _____ or _____ .

2. Write the words from the spelling list that end with the suffix **ence.**

   _____   _____   _____

   _____   _____   _____

   _____   _____   _____

   _____   _____   _____

   _____   _____

3. List the words that have the suffix **ent.**

   _____   _____   _____

B. On a separate sheet of paper, scramble the spelling words. Then trade papers with a partner and unscramble each other's words. Who can solve all 18 words first?

LESSON 30 MORE PRACTICE

The suffixes *ence* and *ent*

1. audience	7. patience	13. difference
2. obedience	8. intelligence	14. coincidence
3. violence	9. influence	15. science
4. silence	10. evidence	16. president
5. absence	11. interference	17. frequent
6. presence	12. circumference	18. delinquent

A. Complete each sentence with a word from the spelling list.

1. I took my dog to _____ school to be trained.

2. Joan had an excused _____ from school.

3. The _____ cheered the remarkable performance.

4. The lawyer presented _____ of the suspect's guilt.

5. It was a _____ that both of us brought the same CDs.

6. Will the politician's campaign _____ the voters?

7. Many people object to the _____ on some TV programs.

8. The crowd watched in complete _____ as the gymnasts performed.

9. The tenant received a notice because he was _____ in paying his rent.

10. Lil's _____ at the meeting was required in order to hold the election.

11. Taking care of very young children requires a great deal of _____.

12. When Angelo got braces, he made _____ trips to the orthodontist.

13. Don measured the _____ of the ball with a string.

14. The _____ we are getting on our radio is caused by the storm.

15. Because of his great _____, Einstein was considered a genius.

16. The _____ between six and four is two.

17. Biology is the _____ of plant and animal life.

18. Our club is preparing to elect a new _____.

B. Each of the following words is contained in one of your spelling words. On a separate sheet of paper, write the word, the spelling word, and a sentence using the spelling word. Do not use any spelling word more than once.

1. flu	**3.** pat	**5.** side	**7.** coin	**9.** deli
2. tell	**4.** bed	**6.** die	**8.** den	**10.** if

LESSON 31 TEACHING
Words ending with *ize* and *ise*

special	+ ize =	special<u>ize</u>	immune	+ ize =	immun<u>ize</u>
central	+ ize =	central<u>ize</u>	harmony	+ ize =	harmon<u>ize</u>
visual	+ ize =	visual<u>ize</u>	monopoly	+ ize =	monopol<u>ize</u>
capital	+ ize =	capital<u>ize</u>			surpr<u>ise</u>
item	+ ize =	item<u>ize</u>			disgu<u>ise</u>
idol	+ ize =	idol<u>ize</u>			telev<u>ise</u>
modern	+ ize =	modern<u>ize</u>			exerc<u>ise</u>
hospital	+ ize =	hospital<u>ize</u>			adv<u>ise</u>
character	+ ize =	character<u>ize</u>			merchand<u>ise</u>

LESSON GENERALIZATION: The suffix **ize** is added to complete words to form verbs meaning "to make or become."

modernize = "to make modern"   centralize = "to make central"

When the suffix is added to complete words, it is usually spelled **ize.**

Notice how a final **e** or **y** is dropped when the suffix is added.

The **ise** spelling is less common. It is usually part of the base word itself rather than a suffix:

surprise   televise

A. Complete the following exercises.

1. The suffix **ize** is usually added to complete words to form verbs meaning "to make or become." Write the words from the list that end in **ize.**

_____   _____   _____

_____   _____   _____

_____   _____   _____

_____

2. The **ise** ending is more often a part of the word than a suffix. Write the words from the word list that end in **ise.**

_____   _____   _____

_____   _____   _____

B. On a separate sheet of paper, write the **ize** and **ise** words in alphabetical order. Check your work with a partner.

LESSON 31 MORE PRACTICE

Words ending with *ize* and *ise*

1. specialize	7. modernize	13. surprise
2. centralize	8. hospitalize	14. disguise
3. visualize	9. characterize	15. televise
4. capitalize	10. immunize	16. exercise
5. itemize	11. harmonize	17. advise
6. idolize	12. monopolize	18. merchandise

A. Decide whether **ize** or **ise** should be added to each word or letter group. Then write the complete word.

1. disgu	_____	**10.** immune	_____
2. central	_____	**11.** surpr	_____
3. character	_____	**12.** item	_____
4. adv	_____	**13.** monopoly	_____
5. merchand	_____	**14.** special	_____
6. harmony	_____	**15.** visual	_____
7. exerc	_____	**16.** idol	_____
8. telev	_____	**17.** modern	_____
9. capital	_____	**18.** hospital	_____

B. Write the spelling word that matches each clue and fits in the boxes.

1. worship
2. bring up to date
3. give an opinion
4. to picture in the mind
5. put in a hospital
6. move vigorously
7. costume
8. pursue a special activity

LESSON 32 Review

thermometer	official	illegible	audience
astrology	occasion	immature	absence
diagram	suggestion	imperfect	frequent
biology	submarine	capitalize	ninety-nine
should've	invisible	hospitalize	
could've	possible	surprise	
hitchhike	eligible	exercise	

A. Complete each analogy with the correct form of a spelling word.

1. **imperfectly** is to **imperfect** as **frequently** is to _____

2. **surprised** is to **surprise** as **capitalized** is to _____

3. **should have** is to **should've** as **could have** is to _____

4. **urban** is to **suburban** as **marine** is to _____

5. **exercising** is to **exercise** as **hitchhiking** is to _____

6. **invisible** is to **visible** as **ineligible** is to _____

7. **possible** is to **impossible** as **perfect** is to _____

8. **capital** is to **capitalize** as **hospital** is to _____

9. **legible** is to **illegible** as **mature** is to _____

10. **surprising** is to **surprise** as **exercising** is to _____

B. Complete each phrase with a word from the list.

astrology	biology	thermometer	absence
should've	occasion	surprise	suggestion
audience	eligible	ninety-nine	invisible

1. _____ been more careful

2. an excused _____ from school

3. read 15° on the _____

4. used a microscope in _____

5. loud applause from the _____

6. _____ years old

7. threw a _____ party

8. an _____ prediction in the paper

9. celebrated the special _____

10. _____ without a telescope

11. not _____ for the team

12. made an excellent _____

LESSON 32 Review

A. Three words in each row follow the same spelling pattern. One word does not. Circle the word that does not fit.

1. intelligible   possible   immovable   audible
2. disguise   obtain   headlight   surprise
3. silence   immature   suppose   advise
4. incredible   impurity   indelible   invisible
5. should've   she'd   three-eighths   could've
6. object   obtain   observe   oppose
7. performance   circumference   obedience   interference
8. astronaut   periscope   hitchhike   biology
9. half-hour   right-handed   wheelchair   double-header
10. hospitalized   itemized   televised   visualized

B. Complete each analogy with a word from the list.

circumference   exercise   audible   submarine
ninety-nine   silence   frequent   windshield
diameter   astronaut   oppose   imperfect

1. **seen** is to **visible** as **heard** is to _____
2. **light** is to **dark** as **noise** is to _____
3. **three** is to **nine** as **thirty-three** is to _____
4. **seldom** is to **infrequent** as **often** is to _____
5. **air** is to **plane** as **water** is to _____
6. **skill** is to **practice** as **fitness** is to _____
7. **line** is to **length** as **circle** is to _____
8. **ship** is to **sailor** as **rocket** is to _____
9. **around** is to **perimeter** as **through** is to _____
10. **agree** is to **support** as **disagree** is to _____
11. **house** is to **window** as **car** is to _____
12. **flawless** is to **perfect** as **damaged** is to _____

Word Parts

The following lists contain common prefixes, suffixes, and Latin and Greek roots. Use these lists to become familiar with the meanings of these word parts.

PREFIXES

The following chart contains prefixes that have only one meaning.

Prefix	Meaning	Example
bene-	good	benefit
circum-	around	circumference
col-, com-, con-, cor-	with, together	collapse, compile, construct, correspond
contra-	opposed	contradict
equi-	equal	equidistant
extra-	outside	extraordinary
hemi-	half	hemisphere
inter-	between, among	international
mal-	bad	maltreat, malignant
mid-	halfway	midday
mis-	wrong	misspell
non-	not	nonworking
post-	after in time or space	postpone
pre-	before	predawn
sub-	under, below	subzero

Some prefixes have more than one meaning.

Prefix	Meaning	Example
a-, ab-	up, out	arise
	not	abnormal
	away	absent
anti-	against	antiaircraft
	prevents, cures	antidote
de-	away from, off	derail
	down	decline
	reverse action of	defrost
dis-	lack of	distrust
	not	dishonest
	away	disarm
em-, en-	to get into, on	embark
	to make, cause	enable
	in, into	enclose
il-, im-, in-, ir-	not	illegal
	in, into	investigate
pro-	in favor of	profamily
	forward, ahead	propel
re-	again	rethink
	back	repay
semi-	half	semicircle
	twice in a period	semiannual
	partly	semiconscious
super-	over and above	superhuman
	very large	supertanker
trans-	across	transcontinental
	beyond	transcend
un-	not	unhappy
	reverse of	unfasten

SUFFIXES

Noun suffixes, when added to a base word or root, form nouns. Become familiar with the following common noun suffixes.

Noun Suffixes That Refer to Someone Who Does Something

Suffix	Examples
-ant	commandant, occupant
-eer	auctioneer
-er	manager
-ician	beautician, statistician
-ist	geologist
-or	counselor

Noun Suffixes That Make Abstract Words

Suffix	Examples
-ance, -ancy, -ence	vigilance, vacancy, independence
-ation, -ion, -ition	imagination, inspection, recognition
-cy	accuracy
-dom	freedom, kingdom
-hood	womanhood, brotherhood
-ice	cowardice, prejudice
-ism	realism, federalism
-ity, -ty	sincerity, frailty
-ment	encouragement, commitment
-ness	kindness, fondness
-ship	ownership, worship
-tude	gratitude, solitude

Adjective suffixes, when added to a base word or root, create adjectives—words that are used to modify nouns and pronouns.

Adjective Suffixes

Suffix	Meaning	Example
-able, ible	able to be	readable, convertible
-al	relating to	musical
-ant	relating to	triumphant
-ar	relating to	polar
-ate	having, full of	passionate
-ful	full of	harmful
-ic	pertaining to, like	heroic
-ish	pertaining to, like	foolish
-ive	pertaining to	descriptive
-less	without	senseless
-like	like	lifelike
-ly	like	scholarly
-most	at the extreme	topmost
-ous	full of	furious

Verb suffixes change base words to verbs. Here are the four most common verb suffixes.

Verb Suffixes

Suffix	Meaning	Example
-ate	to make	activate
-en	to become	strengthen
-fy	to make	simplify
-ise, -ize	to become	merchandise, computerize

Adverb suffixes change base words to adverbs—words that modify verbs, adjectives, and other adverbs. The following chart lists the most common adverb suffixes.

Adverb Suffixes

Suffix	Meaning	Example
-ily, -ly	in the manner of	happily, quickly
-ward	toward	skyward
-wise	like, in the direction of	clockwise

ROOTS

The following two charts show some common Greek and Latin roots.

Useful Greek Roots

Root	Meaning	Example
anthrop	man	anthropology
aster, astr	star	asterisk
auto	self, alone	autobiography
bibl, biblio	book	bibliography
bi, bio	life	biology
chron	time	chronology
dem	people	epidemic
gen	birth, race, kind	generation
geo	earth	geography
gram, graph	write, draw, describe	grammar, paragraph
hydr	water	hydrogen
meter, metr	word, reason, study	dialogue, logic, ecology
neo	new	neoclassical
nom, nym	name, word, law	nominate, antonym
ortho	straight, correct	orthodontist, orthodox
pan	all, entire	panorama
phil	love	philosopher
phob	fear	claustrophobia
phon	sound	phonograph
psych	mind, soul, spirit	psychology
scope	see	telescope
soph	wise	sophisticated
tele	far, distant	television
theo	god	theology
therm	heat	thermometer

Useful Latin Roots

Root	Meaning	Example
capt, cept	take, have	capture, accept
cede, ceed, cess	go, yield, give way	secede, proceed, recess
cred	believe	credit, creed
dic, dict	speak, say, tell	dictate, dictionary
duc, duct	lead	introduce, conductor
fact, fect	do, make	factory, defect
fer	carry	transfer
ject	throw, hurl	eject, inject
junct	join	junction
miss, mit	send	dismiss, admit
mob, mot, mov	move	mobility, motion, movie
meter, metr	measure	barometer
par, para	get ready	prepare, parachute
pon, post, posit	place, put	opponent, deposit
port	carry	porter, portable
puls	throb, urge	pulsate, compulsory
scrib, script	write	prescribe, scripture
spec, spect, spic	look, see	speculate, spectacle, conspicuous
stat	stand, put in a place	statue, state
tain, ten, tent	hold	contain, tenant, attention
tract	pull, move	tractor, retract
ven, vent	come	convention, event
vers, vert	turn	versatile, invert
vid, vis	see	video, vista
voc, vok	voice, call	vocal, invoke
vol	wish	volunteer, malevolent
volv	roll	revolve, involve

Index of Target Words

Word Journal

Word	Meaning	Example in a Sentence

Word	Meaning	Example in a Sentence

Word	Meaning	Example in a Sentence

Word	Meaning	Example in a Sentence

Word	Meaning	Example in a Sentence

Word	Meaning	Example in a Sentence